D0530185

MIGUEL DE CERVANTES SAAVEDRA

DON QUIJOTE
DE LA MANCHA

PRIMERA PARTE

EDICIÓN SIMPLIFICADA PARA
USO ESCOLAR Y AUTOESTUDIO

Esta edición, cuyo vocabulario se ha elegido entre las palabras españolas más usadas (según CENTRALA ORDFÖRRÅDET I SPANSKAN de Gorosch, Pontoppidan-Sjövall y el VOCABULARIO BÁSICO de Arias, Pallares, Alegre), ha sido resumida y simplificada para satisfacer las necesidades de los estudiantes de español con unos conocimientos un poco avanzados del idioma.
El vocabulario ha sido seleccionado también de los libros de texto escolares "Línea", "Encuentros" y "Puente", comparado con "Camino" y "Un nivel umbral" del Consejo de Europa.

Editora: Ulla Malmmose

EDICIÓN A CARGO DE:
Berta Pallares, *Dinamarca*

Cubierta: Per Illum/Mette Plesner
Ilustraciones: Torben Ebbesen

© 1972 por EASY READERS, Copenhagen
- a subsidiary of Lindhardt og Ringhof Undervisning,
an Egmont Company.
ISBN Dinamarca 978-87-23-90273-3
www.easyreader.dk

Easy Readers EGMONT

Impreso en Dinamarca por
Sangill Grafisk Produktion, Holme-Olstrup

MIGUEL DE CERVANTES SAAVEDRA
(1547–1616)

Su condición de soldado le llevó a tomar parte en muchas de las expediciones militares importantes en su época.

Pasó cinco años cautivo en Argel. Su vida estuvo llena de trabajos y de pobreza, pero Cervantes salió de ellos con entereza y dignidad lo que evidencia su carácter heroico y generoso.

Cultivó la poesía y el teatro pero donde alcanza su fama es en el género de la novela. Las dos partes de *El Ingenioso hidalgo don Quijote de la Mancha* (Primera parte 1605, segunda parte 1615) le han dado fama eterna.

En esta obra Cervantes, con melancólica ironía, hace la crítica de la España imperial. A la vez logra con ella una síntesis excepcional de las dos orientaciones que definen el espíritu español: la que valora, sobre todo, los ideales y la que tiene clara conciencia de la realidad. La nota esencial que Cervantes aporta a esta síntesis es que estas dos concepciones no aparecen en su obra como contrarias e irreductibles sino tejidas una en otra como la vida las muestra. Y es que Cervantes supo observar. Por eso sus personajes tienen un tono acabadamente humano. ¿Está loco don Quijote? ¿Está cuerdo? Por encima de toda posible pregunta y de toda posible respuesta está la profunda humanidad del caballero. También Sancho tiene una honda humanidad. La gran verdad humana de los dos personajes hace de ellos no tipos sino seres vivos en los que de una u otra manera puede verse reflejado el hombre. De ahí su trascendencia y su universalidad.

ALGUNAS OBRAS DE CERVANTES

La Galatea (1585). Doce *Novelas ejemplares* (1613) entre las que destacan *El Licenciado Vidriera, La Gitanilla,* y *El coloquio de los perros.*

Entre sus obras teatrales hay que recordar *El retablo de las maravillas, La guarda cuidadosa y Pedro de Urdemalas.*

FRANCIA

San Sebastián

Bilbao

ROVINCIAS
ASCONGADAS
Y NAVARRA

Pirineos

Andorra

CATALUÑA

LA VIEJA

OZaragoza

Barcelona

oriaO

ARAGÓN

MALLORCA

JUEVA

Valencia

ISLAS
BALEARES

CHA

VALENCIA

O
Albacete

MURCIA   Alicante

N

MurciaO

Cartagena

da

ería

Mar Mediterráneo

0   100   250
km

MAPA de la MANCHA

ÍNDICE

DE COMO ERA DON QUIJOTE

En un *lugar* de la *Mancha*, de cuyo nombre no quiero acordarme, no hace mucho tiempo que vivía un *hidalgo* de los de lanza en *astillero*, *adarga* antigua, *rocín* flaco y *galgo* corredor. Tenía en su casa un ama que pasaba de los cuarenta años, una sobrina que no llegaba a los veinte, y un mozo.

Tenía el hidalgo unos cincuenta años, era seco de carnes, seco de rostro, gran *madrugador* y amigo de la caza.

Este hidalgo, en los ratos en que estaba libre (que eran los más del año), se dedicaba a leer *libros de caballerías*, con tanta afición y gusto, que olvidó casi del todo la caza y aun el cuidado de su hacienda; y llegó a tanto su curiosidad y locura en esto, que vendió parte de sus tierras para

adarga   galgo

lugar, pueblo.
Mancha, ver mapa de la Mancha.
hidalgo, persona que, aunque no era noble, se distinguía del pueblo y no vivía de su trabajo.
astillero, construcción de madera u otro material, para apoyar la lanza.
rocín, caballo malo; se dice del que está muy flaco.
madrugador, que madruga; *madrugar*, levantarse muy temprano.
libros de caballerías, ver página 112.

comprar libros de caballerías en los que leer. El pobre caballero perdía el juicio, y se hundió tanto en la lectura de estos libros que se pasaba las noches y los días leyendo; y así, del poco dormir y del mucho leer, se le secó el cerebro. Se le llenó la cabeza de todo aquello que leía en los libros, así de *encantamientos* como de batallas, heri-

---

encantamiento, acción y efecto de *encantar*, hacer maravillas por medio de palabras misteriosas.

das, amores y disparates imposibles, y se le quedó de tal modo en la imaginación que era verdad todo aquello que leía, que para él no había otra historia más cierta en el mundo.

Perdido ya el juicio, *vino a dar en* el más extraño pensamiento en que jamás dio loco alguno en el mundo, y fue que le pareció necesario hacerse caballero andante y, con sus armas y caballo, irse a buscar aventuras y a ejercer todo aquello que había leído que hacían los caballeros andantes, deshaciendo todo género de ofensas y poniéndose en ocasiones y peligros donde, acabándolos, lograse eterno nombre y fama. Y así lo primero que hizo fue limpiar unas armas que habían sido de sus *bisabuelos*.

Fue luego a ver a su rocín, y le pareció que ni el *Bucéfalo* de Alejandro, ni *Babieca* el del *Cid* se igualaban con él. Cuatro días se le pasaron en imaginar qué nombre le pondría, porque (según se decía a sí mismo) no era razón que caballo de caballero tan famoso, y tan bueno como él, estuviese sin nombre conocido; y así, después de muchos nombres que formó y quitó, al fin le vino a llamar Rocinante, nombre, a su parecer, elevado, sonoro y significativo.

Puesto nombre, y tan a su gusto, a su caballo, quiso ponérselo a sí mismo, y en este pensamiento se le pasaron ocho días, y al cabo se vino a llamar don Quijote. Pero, acordándose de que el valiente *Amadís* no se había contentado con llamarse sólo Amadís, sino que añadió el nombre de su patria para hacerla famosa, y se llamó *Amadís de Gaula*, así quiso, como buen caballero, añadir

---

vino a dar en, se le ocurrió.
bisabuelo, padre del abuelo.
Bucéfalo, *Alejandro*, *Babieca*, *Cid*, *Amadís*, *Amadís de Gaula*, ver página 112.

al suyo el nombre de la suya y llamarse don Quijote de la Mancha, con que, a su parecer, honraba a su patria.

Limpias, pues, sus armas, puesto nombre a su rocín y a sí mismo, entendió que no le faltaba otra cosa sino buscar una dama de quien enamorarse; porque el caballero andante sin amores era como árbol sin hojas y sin fruto y como cuerpo sin alma. Decíase él: «Si yo me encuentro por ahí con algún *gigante*, como de ordinario les sucede a los caballeros andantes, y le parto por la mitad del cuerpo o le venzo, ¿no será bien tener a quien enviarle, y que se ponga de rodillas ante mi señora y diga con voz humilde: «Yo, señora, soy el gigante Caraculiambro, señor de la *ínsula* Malindrania, a quien venció en singular batalla el jamás como se debe alabado caballero don Quijote de la Mancha, el cual me mandó que me presentase ante *vuestra merced*, para que vuestra grandeza disponga de mí a su voluntad»? ¡Oh, cómo se alegró nuestro caballero cuando hubo hecho este discurso, y más cuando halló a quien dar el nombre de su dama! Y fue, a lo que se cree, que en un lugar cerca del suyo había una moza labradora de quien él un tiempo estuvo enamorado, aunque ella jamás lo supo. Se llamaba Aldonza Lorenzo, y a ésta le pareció bien darle el título de señora de sus pensamientos; y, buscándole un nombre que se pareciese al de princesa y gran señora, la llamó Dulcinea del Toboso, porque era natural del *Toboso*; nombre, a su parecer, musical, raro y significativo, como todos los demás que a él y a sus cosas había puesto.

---

gigante, hombre mucho más grande de lo normal.

ínsula, forma antigua por isla.

vuestra merced, forma antigua, tratamiento o título de cortesía, hoy, usted.

El Toboso, ver mapa de la Mancha.

Preguntas

1. ¿Quién era don Quijote? ¿Cómo era?

2. ¿Qué nombre se puso a sí mismo? ¿Cómo llamó a su caballo?

3. ¿Qué nombre le dio a su dama? ¿Quién era ésta?

4. ¿Por qué se volvió loco don Quijote?

5. Describa a don Quijote según la ilustración de la página 11.

PRIMERA SALIDA QUE DE SU TIERRA
HIZO DON QUIJOTE

Hecho, pues, todo esto, no quiso aguardar más tiempo a poner en efecto su pensamiento. Y así, sin *dar parte* a persona alguna de su intención y sin que nadie le viese, una mañana, antes del día, que era uno de los del mes de julio, se armó de todas sus armas, subió sobre Rocinante y por la puerta falsa salió al campo, con grandísimo contento de ver con cuánta facilidad había dado principio a su buen deseo. Mas apenas se vio en el campo, cuando le vino un pensamiento terrible, que por poco le hizo dejar la comenzada empresa; y fue que le vino a la memoria que no *era armado caballero* y que, según la ley de la caballería, ni podía ni debía tomar armas con ningún caballero. Esto le hizo dudar; pero, pudiendo más su locura que otra razón alguna, decidió hacerse armar caballero por el primero que encontrase a imitación de otros muchos que así lo hicieron, según él había leído en sus libros. Y así se tranquilizó y prosiguió su camino, sin llevar otro que aquél que su caballo quería, creyendo que en aquello consistía la fuerza de las aventuras.

Casi todo aquel día caminó sin que le sucediera cosa que fuese de contar, de lo cual se desesperaba, porque quisiera encontrarse con quien hacer experiencia del valor de su fuerte brazo. Al anochecer, su rocín y él se hallaron cansados y muertos de hambre; y mirando a todas partes

---

dar parte, avisar.
armar caballero a alguien consistía en hacerle realizar y realizar con él una serie de actos; y una vez hechos, podía obtener el título de caballero.

por ver si descubría algún castillo o *majada de pastores* donde pudiese remediar su mucha necesidad, vio, no lejos del camino por donde iba, una *venta*. Dióse prisa a caminar, y llegó a ella a tiempo que anochecía.

Como a nuestro aventurero todo le parecía pasar al modo que había leído, cuando vio la venta se imaginó que era un castillo. Detuvo a Rocinante, esperando que alguien se pusiese a dar señal de que llegaba un caballero al castillo. Pero como vio que tardaban, se llegó a la puerta de la venta, y vio a dos mujeres mozas que allí estaban, y que a él le parecieron dos hermosas *doncellas* que delante de la puerta del castillo estaban. Estas, como vieron venir a un hombre armado de aquella manera, llenas de miedo se iban a entrar en la venta, pero don Quijote, con voz tranquila, les dijo:

– No huyan *sus mercedes*, ni teman nada; porque a la orden de caballería que profeso no toca hacer ofensa a nadie, y menos a unas doncellas principales como sus mercedes muestran ser. Al oírle, las mozas no pudieron contener la risa; el lenguaje, no entendido por ellas, y la mala figura de nuestro caballero aumentaba en ellas la risa, y en él el *enojo*. Salió el *ventero*, hombre que por ser muy gordo era muy tranquilo, el cual, viendo aquella figura extraña, estuvo a punto de acompañar a las mozas en su risa. Pero determinó de hablarle respetuosamente, y así le dijo:

---

majada de pastores, lugar donde se recoge de noche el *ganado* – los animales – y donde viven los *pastores*, hombres que cuidan el ganado.
venta, casa que estaba en los caminos y lugares alejados de los pueblos para que la gente pudiese descansar en ella.
doncella, mujer virgen.
sus mercedes, ustedes.
enojo, disgusto.
ventero, persona que tiene a su cargo el cuidado de la venta.

– Si vuestra merced, señor caballero, busca *posada*, menos cama (porque en esta venta no hay ninguna), todo lo demás lo hallará en ella en mucha abundancia. Don Quijote respondió:

– Para mí, señor *castellano*, cualquier cosa basta. Pensó el ventero que el haberle llamado castellano había sido por creer que él era de *Castilla*, aunque él era *andaluz*.

Don Quijote se bajó del caballo con mucha dificultad y trabajo, ya que en todo aquel día no había probado *bocado*.

Dijo luego al ventero que tuviese mucho cuidado con su caballo, porque era el mejor del mundo. Miróle el ventero y no le pareció tan bueno como don Quijote decía, ni aun la mitad. Después de dejar el caballo, volvió a ver lo que don Quijote mandaba, al cual las doncellas, que ya se habían hecho amigas de él, le estaban quitando las armas. Luego le preguntaron si quería comer alguna cosa.

– Cualquiera comería yo – respondió don Quijote –, porque cualquiera me iría muy bien.

Pusiéronle la mesa a la puerta de la venta, porque allí hacía más fresco, y el ventero le trajo un pedazo de mal cocido *bacalao* y un pan negro y viejo como sus armas.

---

posada, lugar donde, pagando, se puede comer y dormir.
castellano, señor de un castillo; en ese sentido lo toma don Quijote. Natural de Castilla, así lo toma el ventero.
Castilla, ver mapa.
andaluz, natural de Andalucía, ver mapa.
bocado, un poco de comida.
bacalao, pescado; era una comida muy popular.

Preguntas

1. ¿En qué mes del año salió don Quijote en busca de aventuras?

2. ¿Por qué – según don Quijote – era necesario ser armado caballero?

3. ¿A dónde llegó don Quijote cuando anochecía?

4. ¿Cómo vio don Quijote la venta y a sus habitantes?

5. ¿Qué comió don Quijote?

DON QUIJOTE FUE ARMADO CABALLERO.

Lo que más le fatigaba a don Quijote era el no verse armado caballero; y así, llevado de este pensamiento, se dio prisa a terminar la cena, la cual acabada, llamó al ventero y se puso de rodillas ante él diciéndole:

– No me levantaré jamás de donde estoy, valiente caballero, hasta que vuestra cortesía me conceda el favor que quiero pedirle, el cual resultará en alabanza *vuestra* y en provecho del género humano.

El ventero, que vio a don Quijote a sus pies y oyó semejantes razones, estaba confuso mirándole, sin saber qué hacer ni qué decirle, y le rogaba que se levantase; pero don Quijote no quería hacerlo, hasta que el ventero tuvo que decirle que él le concedía el don pedido.

– No esperaba yo menos de vuestra grandeza, señor mío – respondió don Quijote –; y así os digo que el favor que os he pedido, y que de vuestra liberalidad me ha sido concedido, es que mañana me habéis de armar caballero, y esta noche en este castillo yo *velaré las armas*.

El ventero que era un poco burlón, y ya tenía algunas sospechas de la falta de juicio de don Quijote, para tener de qué reír aquella noche, determinó seguirle el humor, y le dijo que era muy justo lo que deseaba y pedía, y que todo se haría de manera que él quedase armado caballero, y tan caballero, que no pudiese serlo más en el mundo.

Preguntóle si llevaba dineros; respondióle don Quijote

---

vuestra, forma antigua, suya, de usted.

velar las armas, acto que consiste en guardar las armas durante una noche, estando cerca de ellas.

que no los traía, porque él nunca había leído en las historias de los caballeros andantes que ninguno los hubiese llevado consigo. El ventero le dijo que en esto se engañaba: que en las historias no se escribía, por haberles parecido a los autores de ellas que no era necesario escribir una cosa tan clara y tan necesaria de llevarse como eran dineros y camisas limpias; y así, tuviese por cierto que todos los caballeros andantes llevaban esto, por lo que pudiese sucederles; y que también llevaban lo necesario para curar las heridas que recibían, porque no todas las veces en los campos donde combatían y salían heridos, había quien los curase; y por esto le daba por consejo que no caminase de allí en adelante sin dinero y sin las cosas dichas. Don Quijote le prometió hacer lo que le aconsejaba con toda puntualidad; y así se dio orden para que velase las armas en un *corral* grande que a un lado de la venta estaba; don Quijote las puso junto a un pozo, cogió su lanza y comenzó a pasear por delante de las armas *al punto que* comenzaba a anochecer.

Contó el ventero a todos cuantos estaban en la venta la locura del caballero y todos se admiraron de tan extraño género de locura; fueron a mirar a don Quijote y vieron que, con tranquilo ademán, unas veces se paseaba; otras, miraba a las armas, sin quitar los ojos de ellas.

Por la noche uno de los *arrieros* fue a dar agua a sus *mulas* y tuvo que quitar las armas de don Quijote de junto al pozo. Don Quijote, viéndole llegar, en voz alta le dijo:

---

corral, lugar cerrado y descubierto en las casas o en el campo.
al punto que, en el momento en que.
arriero, el que trabaja con animales de carga y los conduce de un lugar a otro.
mula, animal hijo de caballo y burra o de asno y yegua.

— ¡Oh tú, atrevido caballero, que llegas a tocar las armas del más valeroso caballero que *ciñó* espada! Mira lo que haces y no las toques, si no quieres dejar tu vida en pago de tu atrevimiento.

El arriero no hizo caso de estas razones. Don Quijote alzó la lanza con las dos manos y dió con ella tan gran golpe al arriero en la cabeza, que le tiró al suelo. Hecho esto, volvió a pasearse con el mismo *sosiego* que antes. Lo mismo sucedió con el segundo arriero que se acercó a dar agua a sus mulas. Al ver lo que sucedía, los compañeros empezaron a tirar piedras sobre don Quijote, el cual no

---

ciñó, pretérito de ceñir.
sosiego, tranquilidad, serenidad.

abandonó las armas. Daba voces el ventero, diciéndoles a todos que don Quijote estaba loco.

El ventero determinó darle la orden de la caballería antes de que sucediese otra desgracia, y le dijo que ya había cumplido en lo de velar las armas, que con solas dos horas de vela se cumplía, y que, por lo tanto, iba a armarle caballero.

Contestóle don Quijote que él estaba allí para obedecerle en todo y que acabase lo más pronto que pudiese.

El ventero trajo luego un libro donde escribía las compras que le hacían los arrieros, y con una vela que le trajo un muchacho, y con las dos ya dichas doncellas, se dirigió a donde don Quijote estaba, al cual mandó ponerse de rodillas, y, leyendo en su libro como si dijese alguna oración, alzó la mano y le dio sobre el cuello un buen golpe, y tras él, otro con la espada, siempre moviendo los labios como si rezara. Hecho esto, mandó a una de aquellas doncellas que le ciñese la espada, la cual lo hizo con mucha gracia. Luego la otra le puso las *espuelas*.

Hecho esto, don Quijote, deseoso de salir buscando aventuras, *ensilló* a Rocinante, montó en él y abrazando al ventero, le dijo las cosas más extrañas, dándole las gracias por haberle armado caballero. El ventero, deseoso de verle ya fuera de la venta, respondió a las palabras de don Quijote y le dejó irse en buena hora, sin pedirle el dinero de la comida.

espuelas

---

ensillar, ponerle la silla al caballo.

Preguntas

1. ¿Qué le pidió don Quijote al ventero?

2. ¿Cómo era el ventero?

3. ¿Qué cosas debían llevar consigo los caballeros andantes, según el ventero?

4. ¿Quiénes llegaron a la venta?

5. ¿Por qué se enfadó don Quijote con el arriero?

6. ¿Qué hicieron los arrieros?

7. ¿Qué les decía el ventero?

8. ¿Cómo fue armado caballero don Quijote?

9. ¿Qué le dijo don Quijote al ventero?

DE LO QUE LE SUCEDIÓ A DON QUIJOTE CUANDO SALIÓ DE LA VENTA

Don Quijote salió de la venta contentísimo de verse armado caballero. Mas, viniéndole a la memoria los consejos del ventero a cerca de lo que debía llevar consigo, especialmente los dineros y camisas, determinó volver a su casa y ordenar como tener todo lo necesario. También pensaba recibir como *escudero* a un labrador vecino suyo, que era pobre y con hijos, pero muy a propósito para el oficio de escudero. Con este pensamiento guió a Rocinante hacia la aldea, el cual, casi conociendo el camino, con tanta gana comenzó a caminar, que parecía que no ponía los pies en el suelo.

Habiendo andado durante largo rato descubrió don Quijote mucha gente, que, como después se supo, eran unos *mercaderes toledanos* que iban a comprar seda a *Murcia*.

escudo

---

escudero, hombre que llevaba el escudo del caballero cuando éste no lo usaba.

mercader, comerciante, el que compra y vende algo.

toledano, natural de Toledo; ver mapa.

Murcia, ver mapa.

 estribos

Eran seis, y venían con cuatro criados a caballo y tres mozos de mulas a pie.

Apenas los vio don Quijote, cuando se imaginó ser cosa de nueva aventura. Y así, se afirmó bien en los *estribos*, apretó la lanza, llegó la adarga al pecho y, puesto en la mitad del camino, estuvo esperando que aquellos caballeros andantes llegasen, que ya él los tenía por tales; y cuando se acercaron y se pudieron ver y oír, levantó don Quijote la voz y dijo:

– Todo el mundo se detenga, si todo el mundo no confiesa que no hay en el mundo todo mujer más hermosa que Dulcinea del Toboso.

Paráronse los mercaderes al ver la extraña figura del que tales palabras decía, y por la figura y lo que decía, vieron la locura de su dueño; mas quisieron ver despacio en qué acabaría aquella confesión que se les pedía, y uno de ellos, que era un poco burlón, le dijo:

– Señor caballero, nosotros no conocemos quién sea esa buena señora; muéstrenosla vuestra merced, y si ella fuere de tanta hermosura como vuestra merced dice, de buena gana confesaremos la verdad que por parte vuestra nos es pedida.

– Si os la mostrara – replicó don Quijote –, ¿qué hiciérais vosotros en confesar una verdad tan clara? La importancia está en que sin verla lo habéis de creer, confesar, afirmar y defender; y de lo contrario, ya vengáis uno a uno, como pide la orden de la caballería, ya todos juntos, como es mala costumbre entre gente de vuestra clase, aquí os espero, confiado en la razón que tengo de mi parte.

– Señor caballero – replicó el mercader –, suplico a vuestra merced en nombre de todos estos príncipes que aquí estamos, que, porque no carguemos nuestras conciencias confesando una cosa jamás vista ni oída por nosotros, vuestra merced nos muestre algún retrato de esa señora, aunque sea como un grano de trigo; y quedaremos con esto satisfechos y seguros, y vuestra merced quedará contento; y aun creo que estamos tan de su parte que, aunque su retrato nos muestre que es *tuerta* de un ojo, por complacer a vuestra merced, diremos en su favor todo lo que quisiere.

Don Quijote respondió lleno de cólera: – Vosotros pagaréis la gran ofensa que habéis hecho a tan gran belleza como es la de mi señora.

Y al decir esto, *arremetió* con la lanza baja contra el que lo había dicho, con tal fuerza, que, si la buena suerte no hiciera que en la mitad del camino tropezara y cayera Rocinante, lo pasara mal el atrevido mercader. Cayó Rocinante y también su amo y queriéndose levantar, jamás pudo porque se lo impedían las armas. Y mientras luchaba por levantarse y no podía, estaba diciendo:

–No huyáis, mala gente, que no por culpa mía, sino por la de mi caballo, estoy aquí caído.

Un mozo de los que allí venían se acercó a él, cogió la lanza, la hizo pedazos, y con uno de ellos empezó a darle muchos palos a don Quijote. Sus amos le daban

---

tuerto, que le falta la vista en un ojo.
arremeter, acometer, atacar, dirigirse con fuerza y cólera contra una cosa o contra una persona.

voces que no le diese tanto y que le dejase, pero él siguió dándole.

Cansóse el mozo, y los mercaderes siguieron su camino, llevando qué contar en todo él del pobre don Quijote; el cual, cuando se vio solo, probó otra vez a levantarse, pero no pudo.

Preguntas

1. ¿Qué hizo don Quijote cuando salió de la venta?

2. ¿A quién pensaba recibir como escudero?

3. ¿Con quién se encontró don Quijote?

4. ¿Qué les ordenó don Quijote a los mercaderes?

5. ¿ Qué le respondió uno de ellos?

6. ¿Por qué se enfadó don Quijote?

7. ¿Qué le hizo el mozo a don Quijote?

DON QUIJOTE ES LLEVADO A SU ALDEA

Viendo pues que no podía moverse, decidió acudir a su ordinario remedio, que era pensar en algún suceso de los que había leído en sus libros, y su locura le trajo a la memoria aquel de *Valdovinos*, cuando *Carloto* le dejó herido en la montaña; y así, con señales de gran sentimiento, comenzó a decir con debilitado aliento lo mismo que el herido caballero del bosque:

> ¿Dónde estás, señora mía,
> que no te duele mi mal?
> O no lo sabes, señora,
> o eres falsa y *desleal*.

Y de esta manera fue siguiendo el romance, hasta aquellos versos que dicen:

> ¡Oh noble *Marqués* de Mantua,
> mi tío y señor ...

Valdovinos, personaje del romancero, colección de romances, composiciones poéticas en las que se cuenta un suceso.
Carloto, personaje del romancero.
desleal, no leal, no fiel.
marqués, título de nobleza.

Y quiso la suerte que, cuando llegó a este verso, pasara por allí un labrador de su mismo lugar y vecino suyo, que venía de llevar trigo al molino; el cual, viendo a aquel hombre allí caído, se llegó a él y le preguntó quién era y qué mal sentía, que de manera tan triste se quejaba. Don Quijote creyó, sin duda, que aquél era el Marqués de Mantua, su tío, y siguió con el romance, contando su desgracia de la misma manera que el romance lo canta.

El labrador estaba admirado oyendo aquellas locuras y, cuando le limpió el rostro, que tenía cubierto de polvo y lo conoció, le dijo:

– Señor Quijano – que así se debía llamar cuando él tenía juicio y no había pasado de hidalgo a caballero andante – ¿quién ha puesto a vuestra merced de esta manera?

Pero don Quijote seguía con su romance. Viendo esto el buen hombre, le miró por ver si tenía alguna herida, y procuró levantarle del suelo, y con no poco trabajo le subió sobre su *jumento*, por parecerle caballería más sosegada. Recogió las armas, las puso sobre Rocinante y se puso en camino hacia su pueblo, pensativo al oír los disparates que don Quijote decía; y no menos pensativo iba don Quijote, que no se podía tener sobre el burro, y daba unos suspiros tan grandes, que obligaron al labrador a preguntarle cómo se sentía.

Llegaron al lugar, a la hora que anochecía; pero el labrador aguardó a que fuese algo más de noche, para que no viesen al hidalgo tan mal caballero. Llegada, pues, la hora que le pareció, entró en el pueblo, y se dirigió a casa de don Quijote; en ella estaban el cura y el barbero del lugar, que eran grandes amigos de don

---

jumento, asno, burro.

Quijote, a los cuales les estaba diciendo el ama a grandes voces:

– ¿Qué le parece a vuestra merced, señor *licenciado* Pedro Pérez – que así se llamaba el cura –, de la desgracia de mi señor? Tres días hace que no aparecen él, ni el rocín, ni la adarga, ni la lanza, ni las armas. Estos malditos libros de caballerías que él tiene y suele leer tan de ordinario, le han vuelto el juicio; que ahora recuerdo haberle oído muchas veces, hablando solo, que quería hacerse caballero andante e irse a buscar aventuras por el mundo. Malditos sean tales libros, que han echado a perder el más delicado entendimiento que había en toda la Mancha.

Todo esto lo estaba oyendo el labrador, y con ello acabó de entender la enfermedad de su vecino don Quijote. El labrador comenzó a dar voces, diciendo que le abrieran. A sus voces salieron todos, y como conocieron los unos a su amigo, las otras a su amo y tío, que aún no se había bajado del jumento, porque no podía, corrieron a abrazarle. Él dijo:

– Deténganse todos, que vengo mal herido por culpa de mi caballo. Llévenme a mi lecho y llámese, si fuese posible, a la sabia *Urganda*, para que cure mis heridas.

Lleváronle luego a la cama, y no le hallaron ninguna herida.

Hiciéronle a don Quijote mil preguntas, y a ninguna quiso responder otra cosa sino que le diesen de comer y le dejasen dormir, que era lo que más le importaba. Hízose así y el cura preguntó al labrador el modo en que había hallado a don Quijote. Él se lo contó todo,

---

licenciado, en los tiempos antiguos, el que vestía con ropas largas y que había obtenido el título para poder enseñar algo; en este último sentido se usa también hoy; se llamaba así al cura.

Urganda, protectora de Amadís de Gaula.

con los disparates que al encontrarle y al traerle había dicho, lo cual puso más deseo en el cura de hacer lo que al día siguiente hizo, que fue llamar a su amigo el barbero, *maese* Nicolás, con el cual se fue a casa de don Quijote cuando éste todavía estaba durmiendo.

---

maese, forma antigua, maestro.

Preguntas

1. ¿Qué hizo don Quijote cuando vio que no podía moverse?

2. ¿Quién pasó por donde estaba don Quijote?

3. ¿Qué hizo el labrador cuándo llegó al pueblo?

4. ¿Qué le decía el ama de don Quijote al cura?

5. ¿Qué dijo don Quijote cuando llegó a su casa?

DE LO QUE EL CURA Y EL BARBERO
HICIERON CON LOS LIBROS DE DON QUIJOTE

El cura pidió a la sobrina las llaves del *aposento* donde estaban los libros autores del daño, y ella se las dio de muy buena gana; entraron todos dentro, y el ama con ellos, y encontraron más de cien libros grandes y otros pequeños.

El cura mandó al barbero que le fuese dando aquellos libros uno a uno, para ver de qué trataban, pues podía ser que hallaran alguno que no mereciese el castigo del fuego.

No – dijo la sobrina –, no hay que perdonar a ninguno; mejor será arrojarlos por la ventana al patio y quemarlos.

Lo mismo dijo el ama, pero el cura no quiso hacerlo sin primero leer siquiera los títulos. Y el primero que maese Nicolás le dio fue el de Amadís de Gaula, y el cura dijo:

– Este libro fue el primero de caballerías que se imprimió en España, y todos los demás han tomado principio y origen de éste; y así me parece que le debemos condenar al fuego.

– No, señor – dijo el barbero –, porque es el mejor de todos los libros que de este género se han escrito; y así, como a único en su arte, se debe perdonar.

– Por esta razón – dijo el cura – se le concede la vida por ahora. Veámos ese otro que está junto a él.

Después de ver otros cuantos, sin querer cansarse más el cura en leer libros de caballerías, mandó al ama que tomase todos los grandes y los echase al corral. El ama,

---

aposento, habitación, cuarto.

tomando casi ocho de una vez, los arrojó por la ventana. Por tomar muchos juntos, se le cayó uno a los pies del barbero, que quiso saber de quién era, y vio que decía: «Historia del famoso caballero *Tirante el Blanco*».

¡Válgame Dios! – dijo el cura, dando una gran voz –. Dádmelo acá, vecino, que he hallado en él un tesoro. Por su estilo, éste es el mejor libro del mundo: aquí comen los caballeros, duermen y mueren en sus camas, con otras cosas de que todos los demás libros de este género carecen.

– ¿Y qué haremos – dijo el barbero – de estos pequeños libros que quedan?

– Estos – dijo el cura – no deben de ser de caballerías, sino de poesía. Estos no merecen ser quemados, como los demás, porque no hacen ni harán el daño que los de caballerías han hecho.

– ¡Ay, señor! – dijo la sobrina. Bien los puede vuestra merced mandar quemar como a los demás; porque quizá habiendo sanado mi señor tío de la enfermedad caballeresca, leyendo éstos, se le ocurriese hacerse pastor y andar por los bosques cantando, y, lo que sería peor, hacerse poeta, que, según dicen, es enfermedad que no se cura.

– Verdad dice esta doncella – dijo el cura –.

Estando en esto, comenzó a dar voces don Quijote diciendo:

– Aquí, aquí, valientes caballeros; aquí es necesario mostrar la fuerza de vuestros brazos.

Por acudir a estas voces, no siguieron adelante con el examen de los libros que quedaban.

Cuando llegaron a donde don Quijote estaba, ya él es-

Tirante el Blanco, ver página 112.
¡Válgame Dios!, valer, ayudar, frase exclamativa que se emplea para mostrar asombro.

taba levantado de la cama, y seguía dando voces. Le volvieron por fuerza al lecho; diéronle de comer, y quedóse otra vez dormido, y ellos, admirados de su locura.

Aquella noche quemó el ama cuantos libros había en el corral y en toda la casa.

Uno de los remedios que el cura y el barbero dieron, por entonces, para el mal de su amigo, fue que le *tapiasen* el aposento de los libros, para que cuando se levantase no los encontrara; y así fue hecho con mucha prisa. Dos días después se levantó don Quijote, y lo primero que hizo fue ir a ver a sus libros; y como no encontrara el aposento donde lo había dejado, andaba de una a otra parte buscándolo. Llegaba a donde estaba la puerta antes, tocaba la pared con las manos y miraba a todas partes sin decir una sola palabra. Al cabo de un rato, le preguntó

---

tapiar, cerrar la puerta con una pared hecha con tierra (tapia).

a su ama hacia qué parte estaba el aposento de los libros. El ama, que ya estaba advertida de lo que había de responder, le dijo:

– ¿Qué aposento busca vuestra merced? Ya no hay aposento ni libros en esta casa, porque todo se lo llevó el mismo diablo.

– No era el diablo – replicó la sobrina –, sino un encantador que vino sobre una nube, después del día que vuestra merced de aquí se fue. Entró en el aposento, y no sé qué hizo dentro. Al rato salió volando y la casa quedó llena de humo. Cuando fuimos a mirar lo que había hecho no vimos libros ni aposento; sólo nos acordamos muy bien que, aquel mal viejo, dijo en altas voces cuando salía que, por *enemistad* secreta que tenía al dueño de aquellos libros y aposento, dejaba hecho en aquella casa el daño que después se vería. Dijo también que se llamaba el sabio Muñatón.

– *Frestón* diría – dijo don Quijote.

– No sé – respondió el ama – si se llamaba Frestón o Fritón; sólo sé que acabó en 'tón' su nombre.

– Así es – dijo don Quijote –; éste es un sabio encantador, gran enemigo mío, que me tiene *ojeriza* porque sabe que he de luchar con un caballero a quien él favorece y que le he de vencer sin que él lo pueda evitar.

El ama y la sobrina no quisieron replicarle más, y le dejaron solo.

---

enemistad, no amistad.
Frestón, ver página 112.
ojeriza, mala voluntad contra alguien.

Preguntas

1. ¿Qué hicieron el cura y el barbero con los libros de don Quijote?

2. ¿Cuál fue el libro que el barbero le dio al cura?

3. ¿Cuál libro pareció el mejor al cura y por qué?

4. ¿Qué remedio dieron el cura y el barbero para el mal de don Quijote?

5. ¿Cómo le hicieron creer a don Quijote que el encantador se había llevado los libros?

6. ¿Qué motivos tenía Frestón, según don Quijote, para hacer lo que hizo?

DE LA SEGUNDA SALIDA DE
DON QUIJOTE Y DE LA AVENTURA
DE LOS MOLINOS DE VIENTO

Quince días estuvo don Quijote en casa muy sosegado. Sin embargo, en este tiempo solicitó a un labrador vecino suyo, hombre de bien, pero poco inteligente, que le sirviese de escudero. Tanto le dijo, tanto le prometió, que el pobre determinó seguirle.

Decíale, entre otras cosas, don Quijote que se dispusiese a ir con él de buena gana, porque tal vez le podía suceder alguna aventura en que ganase alguna ínsula y le dejase a él por gobernador de ella. Con estas promesas y otras tales, Sancho Panza, que así se llamaba el labrador, dejó a su mujer y a sus hijos y se fue como escudero de su vecino.

Dio luego don Quijote orden de buscar dineros. Vendiendo una cosa, empeñando otra y malvendiéndolas todas, reunió una razonable cantidad. Avisó a su escudero Sancho del día y la hora que pensaba ponerse en camino, para que él se buscase lo que le fuera más necesario; sobre todo le encargó que llevase *alforjas*. Él dijo que las llevaría, y que también pensaba llevar un asno que tenía muy bueno, porque él no estaba acostumbrado a andar mucho a pie. Don Quijote *se proveyó de* camisas y de las demás cosas que él pudo, conforme al consejo que el ventero

alforjas

proveerse de, juntar las cosas necesarias para algo.

le había dado; todo lo cual hecho y cumplido, sin despedirse Panza de sus hijos y mujer, ni don Quijote de su ama y sobrina, una noche se salieron del lugar sin que persona los viese; en la cual caminaron tanto, que al amanecer estuvieron seguros de que no los hallarían aunque los buscasen.

Iba Sancho Panza sobre su asno con sus alforjas y su *bota*, con mucho deseo de verse gobernador de la ínsula que su amo le había prometido. Acertó don Quijote a tomar el mismo camino que había tomado en su primer viaje, por el *campo de Montiel*, y caminaba con menos pena que la vez pasada porque, por ser la hora de la mañana, los rayos del sol no le fatigaban. Dijo *en esto* Sancho a su amo:

bota

– Mire vuestra merced, señor caballero andante, que no se le olvide lo que me tiene prometido de la ínsula; que yo la sabré gobernar, aunque sea grande.

A lo cual respondió don Quijote:

– Has de saber, amigo Sancho Panza, que fue costumbre muy usada de los caballeros andantes antiguos hacer gobernadores a sus escuderos de las ínsulas o reinos que ganaban, y yo tengo determinado de que por mí no falte tan agradecida costumbre; antes pienso llevar ventaja en ella: porque ellos, algunas veces, esperaban a que sus escuderos fuesen viejos para darles algún título de conde

---

Campo de Montiel, ver mapa de la Mancha.
en esto, entonces, en aquel momento.

de algún valle; pero, si tú vives y yo vivo, bien podría ser que antes de seis días ganase yo tal reino, que tuviese otros a él unidos, para coronarte rey de uno de ellos.

– De esa manera – respondió Sancho Panza –, si yo fuese rey por algún milagro de los que vuestra merced dice, Teresa, mi mujer, sería reina y mis hijos, *infantes*.

– Pues, ¿quién lo duda? – respondió don Quijote.

– Yo lo dudo – replicó Sancho –, porque pienso que, aunque lloviese Dios reinos sobre la tierra, ninguno asentaría bien sobre la cabeza de Teresa Cascajo. Sepa, señor, que no vale para reina.

– *Encomienda* tú este asunto a Dios, Sancho – respondió don Quijote –, que Él dará lo que más le convenga.

En esto, descubrieron treinta o cuarenta molinos de viento que hay en aquel campo, y así como don Quijote los vio, dijo a su escudero:

---

infante, el hijo del rey, nacido después del príncipe, o de la princesa.
encomendar, encargar a alguien que haga alguna cosa o que cuide de ella o de alguna persona.

– La suerte va guiando nuestras cosas mejor de lo que acertáramos a desear; porque ves allí, amigo Sancho Panza, donde se descubren treinta, o pocos más, gigantes, con quienes pienso hacer batalla y quitarles a todos las vidas, con cuyos *despojos* comenzarèmos a ser ricos; que ésta es buena guerra, y es gran servicio de Dios quitar tan mala gente de sobre la tierra.

– ¿Qué gigantes? – dijo Sancho Panza.

– Aquellos que ves allí – respondió su amo – de los brazos largos, que los suelen tener algunos de casi dos *leguas*.

– Mire vuestra merced – respondió Sancho – que aquellos no son gigantes, sino molinos de viento, y lo que en ellos parecen brazos son las *aspas*, que movidas por el viento, hacen andar la piedra del molino.

– Bien parece – respondió don Quijote – que no estás ejercitado en esto de las aventuras: ellos son gigantes; y si tienes miedo, quítate de ahí, y ponte en oración mientras yo voy a entrar con ellos en terrible y desigual batalla.

Y diciendo esto, *dió de espuelas* a su caballo Rocinante,

aspa

---

despojos, lo que el vencedor quita al vencido. De *despojar*, quitarle a alguien una cosa que desea tener.

legua, medida (= 5,5 km).

dar de espuelas, picar con las espuelas al caballo para que corra.

sin atender a las voces que su escudero Sancho le daba,
advirtiéndole que, sin duda alguna, eran molinos de viento,
y no gigantes, aquellos que iba a acometer. Pero él iba
tan convencido de que eran gigantes que ni oía las voces
de su escudero Sancho, ni veía, aunque estaba ya bien
cerca, lo que eran; antes iba diciendo a grandes voces:

– No huyáis, *cobardes* y *viles* criaturas; que un solo caballero es el que os acomete.

Levantóse en esto un poco de viento, y las grandes aspas
comenzaron a moverse; visto lo cual por don Quijote,
dijo:

---

cobarde, que no es valiente.
vil, indigno, no digno.

– Pues aunque mováis más brazos que los del gigante *Briareo*, me lo habéis de pagar.

Y diciendo esto, y encomendándose de todo corazón a su señora Dulcinea, pidiéndole que en tal aventura le *socorriese*, bien cubierto con su *rodela*, arremetió con la lanza a todo correr de Rocinante y se lanzó contra el primer mc lino que estaba delante, dándole una lanzada en el aspa. La volvió el viento con tanta fuerza que hizo la lanza pedazos, llevándose tras sí al caballo y al caballero, que fue rodando por el campo. Acudió Sancho Panza a socorrerle a todo el correr de su asno, y cuando llegó le halló que no se podía mover: tal fue el golpe que dio con él Rocinante.

– ¡Válgame Dios! – dijo Sancho. ¿No le dije a vuestra merced que mirase bien lo que hacía, que no eran sino molinos de viento, y no lo podía ignorar sino quien llevase otros tales en la cabeza?

– Calla, amigo Sancho – respondió don Quijote –; que las cosas de la guerra, más que las otras, están sujetas a continua mudanza; cuanto más que yo pienso, y así es verdad, que aquel sabio Frestón que me robó el aposento y los libros, ha vuelto estos gigantes en molinos por quitarme la gloria de su vencimiento: tal es la enemistad que me tiene; mas, al fin, han de poder poco sus malas artes contra la bondad de mi espada.

– Dios lo haga, como puede – respondió Sancho Panza, ayudándole a levantarse y a subir sobre Rocinante.

 — rodela

---

Briareo, ver página 112.
socorrer, ayudar.

Preguntas

1. ¿Qué le prometió don Quijote a Sancho?

2. ¿De qué cosas se proveyó don Quijote?

3. ¿Qué vieron en el campo?

4. ¿Cómo vio don Quijote a los molinos?

5. ¿Qué les dijo don Quijote a los molinos?

6. ¿Qué le sucedió a don Quijote en esta aventura?

7. Describir la aventura de los molinos.

8. ¿Qué le dijo Sancho a don Quijote?

9. ¿Qué le respondió don Quijote y por qué le respondió así?

LO QUE LE SUCEDIÓ A SANCHO EN LA VENTA QUE DON QUIJOTE PENSABA QUE ERA CASTILLO

Hablando de la pasada aventura don Quijote y Sancho se *pusieron en camino* hacia donde les pareció que podía estar el camino *real*. Y la suerte, que iba guiando bien sus cosas, les ofreció el camino, en el cual descubrieron una venta. Llegaron a ella, pero don Quijote decía que no era una venta sino un castillo. Allí pasaron la noche, y, al día siguiente, don Quijote quiso partir a buscar aventuras, pareciéndole que todo el tiempo que se quedase en la venta era quitárselo al mundo y a los necesitados del favor de su brazo. Con este deseo, él mismo ensilló a Rocinante y *enalbardó* el jumento de su escudero. Subió a su caballo, tomó la lanza y se dispuso a salir.

Le estaban mirando todos los que había en la venta, que eran más de veinte personas. Llamó entonces al ventero, y con voz tranquila le dijo:

– Muchos y grandes son los favores que en este vuestro castillo he recibido, y quedo muy obligado a agradecéroslos todos los días de mi vida. Si os los puedo pagar en vengaros de alguno que os haya hecho alguna ofensa, sabed que ese es mi oficio.

albarda

---

ponerse en camino, dirigirse hacia algún lugar.
real, principal.
enalbardar, poner la *albarda* al burro.

El ventero le respondió con el mismo sosiego:

– Señor caballero, yo no tengo necesidad de que vuestra merced me vengue de ninguna ofensa, porque yo sé tomar la venganza que me parece, cuando me la hacen. Sólo necesito que vuestra merced me pague el gasto que esta noche me ha hecho en la venta, así de la cena y camas como de lo que han comido el caballo y el asno.

– ¿Venta es ésta? – replicó don Quijote.

– Y muy honrada – respondió el ventero.

– Engañado he vivido hasta aquí – respondió don Quijote –; pensé que era castillo, y no malo; pero, pues es así que es venta y no castillo, lo que se podrá hacer por ahora es que perdonéis el pago. Yo no puedo dejar de cumplir lo que dice la orden de los caballeros andantes, de los cuales sé cierto que jamás pagaron comida ni otra cosa en venta donde estuvieron.

– Poco tengo yo que ver en eso – respondió el ventero –; pagueme lo que me debe y deje de hablar de cosas de caballerías; que yo lo único que quiero es cobrar mi hacienda.

– *Vos* sois un mal ventero – respondió don Quijote –. Y salió de la venta sin que nadie le detuviese; y él, sin mirar si le seguía su escudero, se alejó.

El ventero, que vio que se iba y que no pagaba, fue a cobrar de Sancho Panza, el cual dijo que, pues su señor no había querido pagar, tampoco él pagaría.

Quiso la mala suerte de Sancho que entre los que estaban en la venta se hallasen gentes alegres y de buen humor, las cuales se acercaron a Sancho y le bajaron de su asno. Uno de ellos entró a buscar la manta de la cama del ventero y, echándole en ella, alzaron los ojos y vieron que el techo era más bajo de lo que necesitaban para su

vos, ver página 112.

o a donde estaba su amo y llegó triste. Cuando
Quijote, le dijo:

ncho bueno, que aquel castillo o venta es
antado, sin duda; porque aquellos que tan
trataron ¿qué podían ser sino gentes del
creo esto por haber visto que cuando estaba
fue posible bajarme de Rocinante, porque
ner encantado; que te juro, por la fe de
i pudiera subir a la tapia del corral o
nante, se acordaran de la burla para

vengara yo si pudiera, pero no pude;
quellos que se divirtieron conmigo no
tados, como vuestra merced dice, sino
hueso como nosotros; y todos, según
ndo me daban vueltas, tenían sus
e llamaba Pedro Martínez, y el otro
el ventero oí que se llamaba Juan
Así que, señor, el no poder bajarse
a estuvo que en encantamientos.
io de todo esto es que estas aven-
cando al final nos han de traer

general de raza lanar, que se crían y

acción y efectos de encantar.

obra; determinaron, pues, salirse al corral, que tenía por
límite el cielo.

Allí, puesto Sancho en la mitad de la manta, comenzaron
a lanzarle a lo alto y a divertirse con él. Las voces que
daba el pobre Sancho fueron tantas, que llegaron a los
oídos de su amo; el cual, deteniéndose a escuchar atenta-
mente, creyó que alguna nueva aventura se le venía, hasta
que conoció que el que gritaba era su escudero. Se volvió y
llegó a la venta y, viéndola cerrada, dio una vuelta, por

47

ver si hallaba lugar por dónde entrar; no lo halló, pero vio lo que hacían con su escudero. Le vio bajar y subir por el aire, con tanta gracia y tan rápido, que, si la cólera le dejara, pienso que se hubiera reído. Desde encima del caballo comenzó a decir tantas y tan terribles cosas a los que con Sancho se divertían, que no es posible escribirlas. Pero no por ello dejaban los otros de reírse, ni Sancho de quejarse, mezclando las quejas, ya con amenazas ya con súplicas; mas todo ello aprovechaba muy poco, y no le dejaron hasta que no estuvieron cansados. Le trajeron su asno y le subieron encima de él. Sancho salió de la venta muy contento de no haber pagado nada y de haber salido con su intención, aunque lo habían pagado, como siempre, sus espaldas. Verdad es que el ventero se quedó con sus alforjas, en pago de lo que se le debía.

Preguntas

1. ¿Por qué no quiere don Q

2. ¿Qué contesta el venter

3. ¿Qué hacen con San

4. ¿Por qué lo hacen?

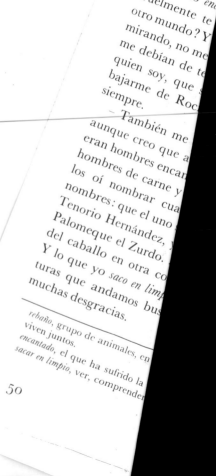

– ¡Qué poco sabes, Sancho – respondió don Quijote –, de cosas de caballerías!

En esta conversación iban, cuando vio don Quijote que por el camino venía hacia ellos una gran *polvareda;* y al verla se volvió a Sancho y le dijo:

– Este es el día, ¡oh Sancho!, en el cual se ha de ver el bien que me tiene guardado mi suerte; este es el día en que se ha de mostrar el valor de mi brazo, y en el que tengo que hacer obras que quedarán escritas en el libro de la fama. ¿Ves aquella polvareda que allí se levanta, Sancho? Pues toda ella está poblada de un grandísimo ejército de diversas e *innumerables* gentes.

– Según eso, dos deben de ser – dijo Sancho –; porque de esta parte contraria se levanta también otra polvareda semejante.

Volvió a mirarlo don Quijote, y vio que así era la verdad. Alegrándose, pensó, sin duda alguna, que eran dos ejércitos que venían a encontrarse en mitad de aquella llanura. La polvareda que habían visto la levantaban dos grandes rebaños de ovejas y carneros, que por aquel mismo camino venían de dos diferentes partes, los cuales, con el polvo, no se vieron hasta que estuvieron cerca. Con tanto empeño afirmaba don Quijote que eran ejércitos, que Sancho llegó a creerlo y a decirle.

– Señor, ¿pues qué hemos de hacer nosotros?

– ¿Qué? – dijo don Quijote –. Ayudar a los necesitados. Y has de saber, Sancho, que este ejército que viene de frente lo conduce y guía el gran Alifanfarón, señor de la gran isla *Trapobana;* y este otro que a mis espaldas marcha

---

polvareda, mucha cantidad de polvo levantado por el viento o por otra cosa.

innumerables, que no se pueden contar.

Trapobana, nombre que se dio antiguamente a la isla de Ceilán.

es el de su enemigo el rey Pentapolín del *Arremangado* Brazo, así llamado porque siempre entra en las batallas con el brazo derecho desnudo.

– ¿Pues por qué se quieren tan mal esos dos señores? –, preguntó Sancho.

– Se quieren mal – respondió don Quijote – porque este Alifanfarón es un *pagano* y está enamorado de la hija de Pentapolín, que es una señora muy hermosa, y es cristiana; su padre no se la quiere entregar al rey pagano si no se hace cristiano.

– Hace muy bien Pentapolín – dijo Sancho –. ¡Yo le ayudaré en todo lo que pudiere!

– En eso harás lo que debes, Sancho – dijo don Quijote –; porque para entrar en batallas semejantes no se necesita ser armado caballero.

– Bien entiendo eso – respondió Sancho –; pero ¿dónde pondremos este asno para que estemos seguros de hallarle después de pasada la batalla?

– Lo que puedes hacer con él – dijo don Quijote – es dejarle a su suerte, se pierda o no, porque serán tantos los caballos que tendremos después, que aun corre peligro Rocinante de que lo cambie por otro. Pero está atento y mira; que te quiero decir quiénes son los caballeros más importantes que en estos dos ejércitos vienen.

– Señor – dijo Sancho –, yo no los veo; quizá todo debe ser encantamiento.

– ¿Cómo dices eso? – respondió don Quijote –. ¿No oyes el *relinchar* de los caballos y el ruido de los *tambores?*

Arremangado, de *arremangar*, recoger, doblándolas hacia arriba, las mangas.

pagano, que no es cristiano.

relinchar, hacer oir el caballo su voz propia, relincho.

tambor

– No oigo otra cosa – respondió Sancho – sino muchos *balidos* de ovejas y carneros.

Y así era en verdad, porque ya llegaban cerca los dos rebaños.

– El miedo que tienes – dijo don Quijote – te hace, Sancho, que ni veas ni oigas bien. Retírate a una parte y déjame solo; yo solo basto para dar la *victoria* a la parte a quien yo dé mi ayuda.

Diciendo esto, espoleó a Rocinante y corrió como un rayo.

Sancho le daba voces, diciéndole:

– Vuélvase vuestra merced, señor don Quijote; que son carneros y ovejas los que va a atacar. ¿Qué locura es ésa? ¿Qué es lo que hace?

Don Quijote en altas voces iba diciendo:

–Ea, caballeros, los que seguís las banderas del valeroso Pentapolín del Arremangado Brazo, seguidme todos: veréis qué facilmente le doy el triunfo sobre su enemigo Alifanfarón.

Diciendo esto, se entró por medio del ejército de las ovejas y comenzó a *alancearlas* con tanto valor, como si de verdad alanceara a su peor enemigo. Los pastores que venían con el rebaño le daban voces que no hiciese

---

balido, voz propia de las ovejas y carneros.
victoria, acto y consecuencia de vencer.
alancear, dar golpes con la lanza, lanzadas; atacar con la lanza.

53

aquello; pero viendo que no les hacía caso, comenzaron a tirarle piedras.

Don Quijote no hacía caso de las piedras sino que, corriendo a todas partes, decía:

– ¿Adónde estás, Alifanfarón? Vente a mí; que un caballero solo soy, que desea probar tus fuerzas y quitarte la vida en castigo de la mala vida que das al generoso Pentapolín.

Llegó en esto una piedra y le dio en un lado. Tan fuerte fue el golpe, que nuestro pobre caballero cayó del caballo. Se llegaron a él los pastores y creyeron que lo habían matado; y así, con mucha prisa recogieron sus rebaños, cargaron los animales muertos, que pasaban de siete, y se fueron.

Todo este tiempo había estado Sancho mirando las locuras que hacía su amo, y maldecía el día y la hora en que le había conocido. Viéndole caído en el suelo, y que ya los pastores se habían ido, se llegó a él. Le encontró muy mal aunque no había perdido el sentido y le dijo:

– ¿No le decía yo, señor don Quijote, que volviese, que los que iba a acometer no eran ejércitos, sino rebaños de corderos?

– Has de saber, Sancho, que aquel sabio, enemigo mío, que me persigue, envidioso de la gloria que vio que yo había de alcanzar de esta batalla, ha vuelto los ejércitos enemigos en rebaños de ovejas. Si no, haz una cosa, Sancho, para que veas que es verdad lo que te digo: sube en tu asno y síguelos; verás como, en cuanto se hayan alejado un poco de este lugar, se vuelven en su ser primero, y, dejando de ser ovejas y carneros, son hombres, tal como yo los vi antes. Pero no vayas ahora, que necesito tu ayuda; llégate a mí y mira cuántas *muelas* y dientes me faltan; que me parece que no me ha quedado ninguno en la boca.

Metió Sancho los dedos en la boca de don Quijote y le preguntó:

– ¿Cuántas muelas solía tener vuestra merced en este lado?

– Cuatro – respondió don Quijote –, todas enteras y muy sanas.

– Mire vuestra merced bien lo que dice, señor – respondió Sancho.

– Digo cuatro, si no eran cinco – respondió don Quijote –; porque en toda mi vida no me han sacado diente ni muela de la boca.

– Pues en esta parte de abajo – dijo Sancho – no tiene vuestra merced más de dos muelas y media; y en la de arriba, ni media, ni ninguna.

– ¡Desgraciado de mí! – dijo don Quijote, oyendo las tristes noticias que su escudero le daba –; que más quisiera

 muela

que me hubiesen derribado un brazo, *como no* fuera el de la espada. Porque te hago saber, Sancho, que la boca sin muelas es como molino sin piedra, y mucho más se ha de estimar un diente que un *diamante*. Pero a todo esto estamos sujetos los caballeros andantes. Sube, amigo, y guía que yo te seguiré al paso que quisieres.

Sancho lo hizo así, y guió a su asno hacia donde le pareció que podrían encontrar una venta sin salir del camino real.

diamante

Preguntas

1. ¿Por qué – según don Quijote – no pudo él socorrer a su escudero?

2. ¿Qué le respondió éste?

3. Describir la aventura de los dos ejércitos.

4. ¿Cuál fue el resultado de esta aventura?

5. ¿Por qué – según don Quijote – eran enemigos los ejércitos?

---

como no, si no.

AVENTURA DEL CUERPO MUERTO

Andando, pues, poco a poco, porque el dolor de las muelas de don Quijote no les permitía ir más *deprisa*, iban hablando don Quijote y Sancho.

Mientras iban hablando, llegó la noche y se hallaron en mitad del camino, sin encontrar una venta donde pasar la noche; y lo peor era que tenían hambre pues todo lo de comer se había quedado en las alforjas. Además de esta desgracia, les sucedió una aventura, que de verdad lo parecía. La noche llegó con alguna obscuridad; pero caminaban, creyendo Sancho que, pues aquel camino era el real, a una o a dos leguas, hallaría en él alguna venta donde poder comer y dormir.

Yendo, pues, de esta manera, el escudero muerto de hambre y el amo con gana de comer, vieron que por el mismo camino por el que iban venían hacia ellos gran número de luces, que no parecían sino estrellas que se movían. Se admiró Sancho al verlas, y don Quijote también; detuvieron uno a Rocinante y el otro al asno, y estuvieron quietos, mirando atentos lo que podía ser aquello. Vieron que las luces se iban acercando a ellos, y cuanto más se acercaban, mayores parecían; a cuya vista, Sancho comenzó a temblar, y aun don Quijote sintió algo de miedo, pero, animándose un poco, dijo:

– Esta, sin duda, Sancho, debe de ser grande y muy peligrosa aventura, donde será necesario que yo muestre todo mi valor.

---

deprisa, de prisa, rápido.
yendo, gerundio de 'ir'.

hacha

litera

Se apartaron los dos a un lado del camino, y miraron con mucha atención lo que aquello de aquellas luces que caminaban podía ser. Al poco rato, descubrieron unos hombres *encamisados*, cuya temerosa vista acabó con el ánimo de Sancho Panza, que comenzó a dar diente con diente, como quien tiene frío; y creció más el miedo cuando vieron, detrás de los encamisados a caballo y con *hachas* encendidas en las manos, una *litera* cubierta de *luto* a la cual seguían otros seis hombres de a caballo, también de luto hasta los pies de las mulas; que bien vieron que no eran caballos en la calma con que andaban. Los encamisados iban hablando entre sí en voz baja. Esto a tales horas y en tal lugar, hubiera bastado para poner miedo en el corazón de Sancho, y aun en el de su amo, si en aquel momento no se le representara en su imaginación que aquélla era una de las aventuras de sus libros.

Se le figuró que en la litera debía de ir algún mal herido o muerto caballero, cuya venganza a él solo estaba reservada y así, se puso bien en la silla y se puso en mitad del camino por donde los encamisados tenían que pasar por fuerza. Cuando los vio cerca, alzó la voz y dijo:

---

encamisado, cubierto desde la cabeza a los pies con una ropa larga.
luto, signos exteriores de pena en las ropas y en los objetos por la muerte de alguien. Hoy el color del luto es negro, en los países de Europa.

– Deteneos, caballeros, y decidme quién sois, de dónde venís, a dónde vais y qué es lo que lleváis en aquella litera. Que, según las señales que veo, vosotros habéis hecho o a vosotros os han hecho alguna ofensa, y conviene y es necesario que yo lo sepa, para castigaros por el mal que hicisteis o para vengaros de la ofensa que os hicieron.

– Vamos deprisa – respondió uno de los encamisados –, está la venta lejos y no nos podemos detener a dar tanta cuenta como vuestra merced pide. Y, habiendo dicho esto, pasó adelante. Don Quijote dijo:

– Deteneos y dadme cuenta de lo que he preguntado; si no, tendréis que luchar conmigo.

La mula se asustó de manera que, alzándose de las *patas* de adelante, tiró a su dueño al suelo. Un mozo que iba a pie, viendo caer al encamisado, comenzó a *insultar* a don Quijote, el cual, sin esperar más, arremetió a uno de los enlutados, lo hirió, y lo tiró al suelo, y empezó a atacar a los demás con tanta rapidez, que parecía que en aquel

---

pata, pierna de los animales.
insultar, dirigir a alguien palabras que le ofenden.

momento le habían nacido alas a Rocinante, según andaba de ligero y contento.

Todos los encamisados eran gente de paz y no llevaban armas, y así en un momento dejaron la batalla y comenzaron a correr por aquel campo con las hachas encendidas. Los enlutados con sus ropas largas no se podían mover, así que don Quijote los *apaleó* a todos y les hizo abandonar el sitio, con lo cual todos pensaron que aquel no era hombre, sino diablo que les salía a quitar el cuerpo muerto que llevaban en la litera.

Todo esto lo miraba Sancho, admirado del valor de su señor, y decía para sí: «Sin duda, este mi amo es tan valiente como él dice».

Estaba un hacha ardiendo en el suelo, junto al primero que derribó don Quijote de la mula, y a la luz del hacha don Quijote pudo verle. Se acercó a él, y poniéndole la punta de la lanza en el rostro, le dijo que *se rindiese*, y que, si no lo hacía, le mataría. A lo cual respondió el caído:

– Bastante rendido estoy, pues no me puedo mover, porque tengo una pierna rota. Suplico a vuestra merced, si es caballero cristiano, que no me mate, que cometerá un gran *sacrilegio*, ya que soy licenciado y he recibido las primeras órdenes.

– ¿Pues quién diablos os ha traído aquí – dijo don Quijote –, siendo hombre de iglesia?

– ¿Quién, señor? – replicó el caído –. Mi desgracia.

– Pues otra mayor os amenaza – dijo don Quijote –, si no me respondéis a todo cuanto os pregunté antes.

---

apalear, dar golpes con un palo o cosa semejante.
se rindiese de rendirse.
sacrilegio, falta grave de respeto contra una cosa o una persona que tiene relación con Dios o con la religión.

– Con facilidad será vuestra merced satisfecho – respondió el licenciado –; y así, sabrá vuestra merced que me llamo Alonso López, vengo de la ciudad de *Baeza* con otros once sacerdotes, que son los que huyeron, y vamos a *Segovia*, acompañando a un cuerpo muerto, que va en aquella litera y que es de un caballero que murió en Baeza, y ahora, como digo, llevamos sus huesos a Segovia, de donde es natural.

– ¿Y quién le mató? – preguntó don Quijote.

– Dios, por medio de una enfermedad – respondió Alonso Pérez.

– Siendo así – dijo don Quijote –, Dios me ha quitado el trabajo de tomar venganza de su muerte, si otro alguno le hubiera matado; pero habiéndole matado quien le mató, hay que callar, porque lo mismo haría si a mi mismo me matara. Y quiero que sepa vuestra merced que yo soy un caballero de la Mancha, llamado don Quijote, y mi oficio es andar por el mundo vengando ofensas y deshaciendo agravios.

– Suplico a vuestra merced – respondió el caído –, señor caballero andante, que me ayude a salir de debajo de esta mula, porque tengo una pierna rota.

– ¿Hasta cuándo esperábais a decirme lo que os pasaba?

Dio luego voces a Sancho, diciéndole que viniese; pero Sancho no vino, porque andaba ocupado cogiendo lo que llevaban en una mula que traían aquellos buenos señores y lo que llevaban eran cosas de comer. Acudió luego a las voces de su amo, y ayudó a sacar a Alonso Pérez de debajo de la mula, y, poniéndole encima de ella, le dio el hacha; don Quijote le dijo que siguiese a sus compañeros y les pidiese perdón de su parte. Sancho le dijo:

Baeza, Segovia, ver mapa.

– Si acaso quisieran saber esos señores quién ha sido el valiente caballero que les puso tal como están, dígale vuestra merced que ha sido el famoso don Quijote de la Mancha, que por otro nombre se llama el Caballero de la Triste Figura.

Con esto se fue Antonio López y don Quijote le preguntó a Sancho qué le había hecho llamarle el Caballero de la Triste Figura.

– Yo se lo diré – respondió Sancho –; porque le he estado mirando un rato a la luz de aquella hacha que llevaba aquel hombre, y verdaderamente tiene vuestra merced la peor figura que jamás he visto, y la causa debe ser el cansancio de esta batalla o la falta de las muelas y dientes.

– No es eso – respondió don Quijote –; sino que al sabio que está encargado de escribir la historia de mis *hazañas* le habrá parecido bien que yo tome algún nombre, como lo tomaban todos los caballeros de antes. Y así él te habrá puesto ahora en la lengua y en el pensamiento que me llamases el Caballero de la Triste Figura, como pienso llamarme desde hoy.

Quería don Quijote mirar si el cuerpo que iba en la litera eran huesos o no; pero Sancho no lo consintió, diciéndole:

– Señor, vuestra merced ha acabado esta peligrosa aventura mejor que ninguna de las que yo he visto. Esta gente, aunque vencida, podría ser que se diese cuenta de que los venció una sola persona, y que volviesen a buscarnos. La montaña está cerca, el hambre se hace sentir; no hay que hacer sino retirarnos.

Y cogiendo su asno rogó a su señor que le siguiese; el cual, viendo que Sancho tenía razón, le siguió sin replicar.

---

hazaña, acción para la que es necesario mucho valor.

Después de haber caminado un poco entre montañas, se hallaron en un valle escondido y tranquilo, donde se detuvieron y tendidos sobre la verde hierba, comieron, satisfaciendo sus estómagos.

Pero les sucedió otra desgracia, y Sancho pensó que era la peor de todas, y fue que no tenían vino que beber, ni aun agua.

Preguntas

1. ¿Qué vieron don Quijote y Sancho, que les causó miedo?

2. ¿Quiénes eran los personajes que encontraron?

3. ¿A dónde iban?

4. ¿Qué llevaban en la litera?

5. ¿Quién era A. López y qué le contó a don Quijote?

QUE TRATA DE LA AVENTURA DEL
YELMO DE MAMBRINO

Cuando acabaron de comer prosiguieron su camino. No habían andado mucho cuando descubrió don Quijote un hombre a caballo, que traía en la cabeza una cosa que *relumbraba* como si fuese de oro; y apenas le hubo visto, cuando se volvió a Sancho y le dijo:

– Sancho: «Donde una puerta se cierra, otra se abre». Te digo esto porque si anoche nos cerró la suerte la puerta de la que buscábamos, ahora nos abre otra para mejor y más cierta aventura, que si yo no acertare a entrar por ella, mía será la culpa. Digo esto porque, si no me engaño, hacia nosotros viene uno que trae en su cabeza puesto el yelmo de Mambrino.

– Mire vuestra merced bien lo que dice, y mejor lo que hace – respondió Sancho –, que yo creo que vuestra merced se engaña en lo que dice.

– ¿Cómo me puedo engañar en lo que digo? – dijo don Quijote. Dime ¿no ves aquel caballero que hacia nosotros viene, sobre un caballo, y que trae puesto en la cabeza un yelmo de oro?

– Lo que yo veo – respondió Sancho – no es sino un hombre sobre un asno, que trae sobre la cabeza una cosa que brilla.

yelmo

---

relumbrar, brillar mucho.
yelmo de Mambrino, yelmo encantado que llevaba el rey Mambrino.

bacía

– Pues ése es el yelmo de Mambrino – dijo don Quijote –. Apártate y déjame con él a solas; verás cómo sin hablar palabra concluyo esta aventura y queda por mío el yelmo.

Era, pues, el caso que el yelmo y el caballo y el caballero que don Quijote veía era esto: que en aquellos alrededores había dos aldeas, la una tan pequeña que no tenía *botica* ni barbero, y la otra, que estaba junto a ella, sí; y así, el barbero de la mayor servía a la menor, en la cual tuvo necesidad uno de *hacerse la barba*, para lo cual venía el barbero y traía una *bacía* de *azófar;* y quiso la suerte que, al tiempo que venía, comenzó a llover, y porque no se le manchase el sombrero, que debía de ser nuevo, se puso la bacía sobre la cabeza; y, como estaba limpia, desde media legua relumbraba. Venía sobre un asno, como Sancho dijo, aunque a don Quijote le pareciera caballo, y la bacía, yelmo de oro; que todas las cosas que veía las aplicaba con mucha facilidad a sus caballerías y pensamientos. Y cuando él vio que el pobre caballero llegaba cerca, sin hablar con él, a todo correr de Rocinante, arremetió con la lanza, llevando intención de pasarle de parte a parte; cuando ya llegaba cerca de él, sin detener la fuerza de su carrera, le dijo:

–Defiéndete, maldita criatura, o entrégame de tu voluntad lo que con tanta razón se me debe.

---

botica, lugar donde se hacen y se venden medicinas.
hacerse la barba, *afeitarse*, quitar, cortando, los pelos de la barba.
azófar, latón, metal.

celada

El barbero, que, tan sin pensarlo ni temerlo vio venir aquella figura sobre sí, no tuvo otro remedio para poder librarse del golpe de la lanza que dejarse caer del asno abajo. Apenas hubo tocado el suelo, cuando se levantó ligero y comenzó a correr por aquel campo, tan aprisa que no le alcanzara el mismo viento. Dejóse la bacía en el suelo, con la cual se contentó don Quijote. Mandó a Sancho que levantase el yelmo, el cual tomándolo en las manos dijo:

– Por Dios que la bacía es buena.

Y dándosela a su amo, éste se la puso en la cabeza y dijo:

– Sin duda que el pagano a cuya medida se hizo primero esta famosa *celada* debía tener una cabeza muy grande; y lo peor de ello es que le falta la mitad.

Cuando Sancho oyó llamar a la bacía celada, no pudo contener la risa; pero se calló, temiendo la ira de su amo.

– ¿De qué te ríes, Sancho? – dijo don Quijote.

– Me río – respondió él – de pensar en la gran cabeza que tenía el pagano dueño de este yelmo que se parece a una bacía de barbero.

– ¿Sabes qué imagino, Sancho? Que esta famosa pieza de este encantado yelmo, por alguna causa extraña debió de llegar a manos de quien no supo conocer ni estimar su valor y sin saber lo que hacía, viéndola de oro purísimo, debió de quitarle la mitad y de la otra mitad hizo esta que parece bacía de barbero, como tú dices.

– Eso será – dijo Sancho. Pero, dejando eso aparte, dígame vuestra merced qué haremos con el asno que dejó abandonado aquí el hombre que vuestra merced derribó?

– Yo no acostumbro a *despojar* a los vencidos, ni es uso de la caballería quitarles los caballos. Así que, Sancho, deja ese caballo o asno, o lo que tú quisieres que sea; que cuando su dueño nos vea lejos volverá a buscarlo.

Subieron a caballo y se pusieron a caminar por donde la voluntad de Rocinante quiso, que se llevaba tras sí la de su amo y aun la del asno, que siempre le seguía en buen amor y compañía. Con todo esto, volvieron al camino real y siguieron por él.

---

despojar, quitarle a alguien una cosa que desea tener.

Preguntas

1. ¿Qué fue lo que a don Quijote le pareció un yelmo y por qué?

2. ¿Qué le pareció a Sancho que llevaba el hombre sobre la cabeza?

3. ¿Por qué llevaba el hombre la bacía sobre la cabeza y quién era este hombre?

4. ¿Qué le dijo don Quijote al hombre?

5. ¿Qué hizo éste?

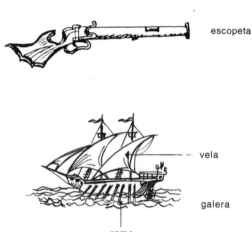

escopeta

vela

galera

remo

QUE TRATA DE LA LIBERTAD QUE DIO
DON QUIJOTE A MUCHOS DESGRACIADOS

Don Quijote alzó los ojos y vio que por el camino que llevaban venían hasta doce hombres a pie sujetos por los cuellos con una gran *cadena*, y todos con *esposas* en las manos. Venían con ellos dos hombres de a caballo y dos a pie; los de a caballo con *escopetas* y los demás con espadas.

Así como Sancho Panza los vio dijo:

– Esta es cadena de *galeotes*, gente forzada del Rey, que van a *galeras*.

– ¿Cómo gente forzada? – preguntó don Quijote –. ¿Es posible que el Rey haga fuerza a alguien?

– No digo eso – respondió Sancho –, sino que es gente que por sus culpas va a la fuerza condenada a servir al Rey en las galeras.

– En resolución – replicó don Quijote –, ¿esta gente, aunque los llevan, no van por su voluntad, van por la fuerza?

– Así es – dijo Sancho.

– Pues de esa manera – dijo su amo – aquí tengo que ejercer mi oficio: ayudar a los miserables.

– Advierta vuestra merced – dijo Sancho – que la justicia, que es el mismo Rey, no hace ofensa a semejante gente, sino que les castiga en pena de sus delitos.

cadena   esposas

galeote, hombre castigado a cumplir su castigo en las *galeras*, barcos antiguos de vela y remo, que pertenecían al rey.

Llegó, en esto, la cadena de los galeotes, y don Quijote, con corteses razones, pidió a los que iban guardándolos que le informasen y dijesen la causa o causas por las que llevaban a aquella gente de aquella manera. Uno de los hombres de a caballo respondió que eran galeotes, gente del Rey, que iban a galeras, y que no había más que decir, ni él tenía más que saber.

– Con todo eso – replicó don Quijote –, querría saber de cada uno de ellos en particular la causa de su desgracia.

Añadió a éstas otras tales y tan amables razones para moverlos a que le dijesen lo que deseaba, que uno de los guardas de a caballo le dijo:

– Vuestra merced se llegue y se lo pregunte a ellos mismos, que ellos se lo dirán si quieren.

Con este permiso, que don Quijote se hubiera tomado si no se lo hubiesen dado, se llegó a la cadena, y les preguntó por qué pecados iban de tan mala manera.

Detrás de todos venía un hombre de muy buen *parecer* de edad de treinta años. Venía atado de una manera diferente a los demás, porque traía una cadena al pie, tan grande, que le rodeaba todo el cuerpo. Preguntó don Quijote cómo iba aquel hombre con tantas cadenas más que los otros. El guarda respondióle que tenía aquel solo más delitos que todos los otros juntos y que era tan atrevido que, aun llevándole de aquella manera, no iban seguros de él.

– ¿Qué delitos puede tener – dijo don Quijote –, si no ha merecido más pena que echarle a galeras?

– Va por diez años – replicó el guarda –, que es como muerte civil. No se quiera saber más sino que este buen

---

parecer, aspecto.

hombre es el famoso Ginés de Pasamonte, que por otro
nombre llaman Ginesillo de Parapilla.

– Señor guarda – dijo entonces el galeote –, váyase poco
a poco y no andemos ahora a explicar nombres y sobrenom-
bres. Ginés me llamo, y no Ginesillo, y Pasamonte es mi
apellido, y no Parapilla.

– Hable con menos tono – replicó el guarda –, señor

ladrón, si no quiere que le haga callar contra su voluntad.

– Algún día sabrá alguno – respondió el galeote – si me llamo Ginesillo de Parapilla, o no.

– Pues ¿no te llaman así? – replicó el guarda.

– Sí, me lo llaman – respondió Ginés –, mas yo haré que no me lo llamen. Señor caballero, si tiene algo que darnos, dénoslo y vaya con Dios; que ya cansa con tanto querer saber vidas ajenas; si la mía quiere saber, sepa que soy Ginés de Pasamonte, cuya vida está escrita por estos dedos.

– Dice verdad – dijo el guarda –, que él mismo ha escrito su historia y deja empeñado el libro en la cárcel por doscientos reales.

Don Quijote, volviéndose a todos los presos dijo:

– De todo cuanto me habéis dicho, hermanos, he sacado en limpio que, aunque os han castigado por vuestras culpas, las penas que vais a padecer no os dan mucho gusto, y que vais a ellas de muy mala gana y muy contra vuestra voluntad. Quiero, pues, rogar a estos señores que os guardan que sean servidos de desataros y dejaros ir en paz.

– ¡Bueno está lo que dice! – replicó el comisario –. Quiere que le dejemos los forzados del Rey, como si tuviéramos autoridad para soltarlos, o él la tuviera para mandárnoslo. Váyase vuestra merced, señor, por su camino.

Don Quijote arremetió contra él con tanta rapidez, que, sin darle tiempo para defenderse, lo tiró al suelo, mal herido de una lanzada; éste era el de la escopeta. Los demás guardianes quedaron asombrados del no esperado suceso; pero, volviendo en sí con rapidez, echaron mano a sus espadas y arremetieron contra don Quijote, que los esperaba con mucha calma, y sin duda lo hubiera pasado mal, si los galeotes, viendo la ocasión que se les ofrecía de alcanzar la libertad, no hubiesen procurado romper la cadena donde venían sujetos. Los guardianes, entre atender que no se escaparan los galeotes y acometer a don Quijote, no hicieron cosa que fuese de provecho. Ayudó Sancho a que se soltara Ginés de Pasamonte, el cual, arremetiendo contra el comisario caído, le quitó la espada y la escopeta e hizo que no quedara guardián alguno en todo el campo, porque todos fueron huyendo, así de la escopeta como de las muchas *pedradas* que los galeotes ya sueltos les tiraban.

Sancho se puso muy triste con este suceso, porque pensó que los que iban huyendo darían cuenta a la *Santa Hermandad*, la cual saldría a buscar a los galeotes, y así se lo dijo a su amo, y le rogó que se marchasen de allí enseguida.

– Bien está – dijo don Quijote –, pero yo sé lo que ahora conviene que se haga. Y llamando a todos los galeotes, les dijo:

– De gente bien nacida es propio agradecer los beneficios que reciben, y una de las cosas que más ofende a Dios es el no ser agradecido. Digo esto porque ya habéis visto, señores, el beneficio que de mí habéis recibido; en pago del cual querría, y es mi voluntad, que, cargados con esa cadena de la que os he librado, vayáis a la ciudad del Toboso, y que allí os presentéis delante de la señora Dulcinea del Toboso y le digáis que su caballero, el de la Triste Figura, es quien os ha dado la libertad. Hecho esto, os podréis ir donde queráis.

---

pedrada, golpe dado por una piedra lanzada contra alguien o contra algo.
Santa Hermandad, ver página 112.

Respondió por todos Ginés de Pasamonte, y dijo:

– Lo que vuestra merced nos manda, señor y libertador nuestro, es imposible cumplirlo, porque no podemos ir juntos por los caminos, sino solos y separados, para no ser hallados por la Santa Hermandad que, sin duda alguna, ha de salir en nuestra busca. Lo que vuestra merced puede hacer es cambiar ese servicio de la señora Dulcinea del Toboso por algún número de oraciones, que nosotros diremos por la intención de vuestra merced; y ésta es cosa que podemos cumplir de noche y de día, en paz o en guerra; pero pensar que hemos de volver ahora a tomar nuestra cadena y a ponernos en camino del Toboso, es pensar que ahora es de noche, cuando todavía no son las diez del día.

– Pues – dijo don Quijote ya puesto en cólera –, don Ginesillo de Paropillo, o como os llaméis, juro que habéis de ir vos solo cargado con toda la cadena.

Pasamonte, que ya estaba enterado de que don Quijote estaba loco, por la locura que había hecho dándoles la libertad, viéndose tratar de aquella manera, hizo señas a sus compañeros, y, apartándose, comenzaron a llover piedras sobre don Quijote. Sancho se puso detrás de su asno, y con él se defendía de la nube de piedras que sobre ambos llovía. No se pudo cubrir tan bien don Quijote, que no le diesen no sé cuántas piedras en el cuerpo con tanta fuerza, que le tiraron al suelo.

Después de esto, los galeotes se fueron cada uno por su lado y quedaron solos el asno y Rocinante, Sancho y don Quijote; el asno, con la cabeza baja y pensativo sacudiendo a veces las orejas, pensando que todavía no había acabado la lluvia de las piedras que le perseguía las orejas; Rocinante, tendido junto a su amo, pues también había ido al suelo de una pedrada; Sancho, temeroso de la Santa Hermandad. Don Quijote, triste por verse tan mal tratado

de los mismos a quienes había hecho tanto bien, dijo a su escudero:

— Siempre, Sancho, he oído decir que hacer bien a pícaros es echar agua al mar. Si yo hubiera creído lo que me dijiste, hubiera evitado estas penas; pero ya está hecho. Paciencia.

Preguntas

1. ¿Qué vio don Quijote en el camino que llevaban?

2. ¿Quiénes eran aquellos hombres?

3. ¿Qué le dijo Sancho a don Quijote sobre aquellos hombres?

4. ¿Qué les preguntó don Quijote?

5. ¿Quién era el último hombre de la fila y qué habló con don Quijote?

6. ¿Qué conclusión sacó don Quijote y qué decidió?

7. ¿Qué le respondió el guarda?

8. ¿Qué hizo entonces don Quijote?

9. ¿Qué le exigía don Quijote a los presos y qué le respondió Ginés?

10. ¿Cómo acabó todo esto?

DE LA *PENITENCIA* DE DON QUIJOTE

Y dicho esto, subió don Quijote sobre Rocinante y, guiando Sancho sobre su asno, se entraron por una parte de *Sierra Morena*, que allí cerca estaba. Llevaba Sancho la intención de atravesarla toda e ir a salir a *Almodóvar del Campo*, y esconderse algunos días por aquellas montañas por no ser encontrados por la Santa Hermandad, si ésta los buscaba.

Aquella noche llegaron a la mitad de Sierra Morena y la pasaron entre muchos árboles. Pero la suerte contraria, que, según opinión de los que no tienen la luz de la verdadera fe, todo lo guía a su modo, ordenó que Ginés de Pasamonte, por el miedo que tenía a la Santa Hermandad, decidiera esconderse en aquellas montañas. Su suerte y su miedo le llevaron al mismo lugar en el que dormían don Quijote y Sancho. Como los malos no son nunca agradecidos, Ginés, que no era agradecido, le robó el asno a Sancho, y antes de que amaneciese estaba lejos de aquel lugar.

Amaneció, y Sancho Panza, viéndose sin su asno, comenzó a llorar con el llanto más triste y más doloroso del mundo.

Don Quijote, que vio el llanto y supo la causa, consoló a Sancho con las mejores palabras que pudo y le rogó que tuviese paciencia, prometiéndole darle una *cédula de cambio*

---

penitencia, obligación que alguien se impone a sí mismo de hacer algo por algún motivo.
Sierra Morena, ver mapa de la Mancha.
Almodóvar del Campo, ver mapa de la Mancha.
cédula de cambio, escrito que se da en un lugar para recibir en otro lo que se indica. Hoy 'letra de cambio'.

maleta   candado

para que le diesen tres asnos, de cinco que don Quijote
había dejado en su casa. Con esto se consoló Sancho y se
limpió las lágrimas agradeciéndole mucho a su señor el
favor que le hacía. A don Quijote, cuando entró por
aquellas montañas, se le alegró el corazón, pues aquellos
lugares le parecían convenientes para las aventuras que
buscaba.

Sancho iba detrás de su amo, y como le pareció que iban
por parte segura, no tenía otra preocupación que comer, y
así iba comiendo sin pensar en aventuras.

Alzó los ojos y vio que su amo estaba parado, procuran-
do levantar algo con la punta de la lanza, por lo cual se
dio prisa a llegar a ayudarle, si fuese necesario, y cuando
llegó, ya don Quijote alzaba con la punta de la lanza una
maleta. Mandóle don Quijote que mirase lo que en la
maleta venía. Sancho lo hizo con mucha rapidez y, aunque
la maleta estaba cerrada con cadena y *candado*, vio por
la parte que se había roto que en ella había cuatro
camisas y, entre unas cosas, unos cuantos *escudos de* oro.
Al verlos, exclamó:

– ¡Bendito sea Dios, que nos ha dado una aventura que
sea de provecho!

Buscando más, encontró un *librito de memoria*. Este se lo
pidió don Quijote y le mandó que se guardase el dinero

---

escudo, moneda.
librito de memoria, cuaderno especial en el que se apuntaban las còsas
para no olvidarlas.

y lo tomase para él. Sancho le besó las manos por el favor que don Quijote le hacía y continuaron su camino a través de la Sierra.

Poco a poco iban entrando en ella. Sancho deseaba hablar con su amo y esperaba que don Quijote comenzase a hablar, hasta que, no pudiendo aguantar tanto silencio, le dijo:

– Señor, ¿es buena regla de caballería que andemos perdidos por estas montañas, sin camino?

– Calla, Sancho – dijo don Quijote –, porque te hago saber que lo que me trae aquí es el deseo de hacer una hazaña, con la cual he de ganar eterno nombre y fama por toda la tierra.

– ¿Es de mucho peligro esa hazaña? – preguntó Sancho.

– No, pero todo ha de estar en tu diligencia, en tu rapidez y en tu cuidado.

– ¿En mi rapidez y cuidado? – dijo Sancho –.

– Sí – dijo don Quijote –; porque, si vuelves pronto de donde pienso enviarte, pronto acabará mi pena y comenzará mi gloria. Y quiero, Sancho, que sepas que el famoso Amadís de Gaula fue uno de los más perfectos caballeros andantes. No he dicho bien; fue él solo el primero, el único, el señor de todos cuantos hubo en su tiempo en el mundo. Y una de las cosas en que este caballero mostró más su valor, sufrimiento y amor, fue cuando se retiró, *desdeñado* por la señora *Oriana*, a hacer penitencia en la *Peña Pobre*, cambiando su nombre por el de Beltenebros. Así que me es a mí más fácil imitarle en esto que no en deshacer ejércitos y deshacer encantamientos. Y, pues,

---

desdeñado, despreciado.
Oriana, dama de Amadís.
Peña Pobre, ver página 112.

estos lugares son excelentes para semejantes cosas, no hay por qué dejar pasar la ocasión que ahora se me ofrece.

– ¿Qué es lo que vuestra merced quiere hacer en este lugar lejano? – preguntó Sancho.

– ¿No te he dicho ya – respondió don Quijote – que quiero imitar a Amadís, haciendo aquí el desesperado y el loco?

– A mí me parece – dijo Sancho –, que los caballeros que hicieron una cosa semejante, tuvieron una causa para hacer esas locuras y penitencias; pero vuestra merced ¿qué causa tiene para volverse loco?

– Ahí está el punto – respondió don Quijote –, y ésa es la delicadeza de mi negocio: volverse loco sin motivo y dar a entender a mi dama que si, sin causa, hago esto ¿qué hiciera con ella? Así que, Sancho amigo, no gastes tiempo en aconsejarme que deje de hacer lo que tengo pensado y te he dicho. Loco soy, loco he de ser hasta que tú vuelvas con la respuesta de una carta que contigo pienso enviar a mi señora Dulcinea; si la respuesta es tal como se debe a mi amor, se acabará mi locura y mi penitencia; pero si fuese lo contrario, seré loco de verdad y, siéndolo, no sentiré nada.

Preguntas

1. ¿Por qué quiere don Quijote hacer penitencia?

2. ¿Quién le robó a Sancho el burro?

3. ¿Qué le dijo don Quijote y cómo le consoló?

4. ¿Qué encontraron dentro de la maleta?

5. ¿Qué quería demostrar don Quijote al hacer la penitencia?

CARTA DE AMOR DE DON QUIJOTE
A DULCINEA

En esta conversación llegaron a una alta montaña, que estaba sola entre otras muchas que la rodeaban. Corría por allí un tranquilo *arroyuelo* y era un lugar tan verde y hermoso que daba alegría a los ojos que le miraban. Había por allí muchos árboles y algunas plantas y flores que hacían el lugar apacible. Este fue el lugar que escogió don Quijote para hacer penitencia. Al verlo, el Caballero de la Triste Figura, comenzó a decir en voz alta, como si estuviera sin juicio:

– Este es el lugar, ¡oh cielos!, que escojo para llorar la desgracia en que vosotros mismos me habéis puesto. ¡Oh Dulcinea del Toboso, día de mi noche, gloria de mi pena, norte de mis caminos! Considera el lugar y el estado en que tu ausencia me ha puesto y corresponde a mi amor. ¡Oh, tú, escudero mío, toma bien en la memoria lo que aquí verás hacer, para que se lo cuentes a mi señora Dulcinea!

Y diciendo esto, se bajó de Rocinante y en un momento le quitó el *freno* y la silla y le dijo:

– Libertad te da el que sin ella queda, ¡oh caballo tan excelente por tus obras como *desdichado* por tu suerte!

freno

---

arroyuelo, río muy pequeño.
desdichado, que no tiene dicha, desgraciado.

Viendo todo esto, dijo Sancho:

– Señor Caballero de la Triste Figura, si mi partida y la locura de vuestra merced van de veras, será bien volver a ponerle la silla a Rocinante, para que *supla* la falta de mi asno, porque será ahorrar tiempo a mi ida y vuelta; si voy andando no sé cuando llegaré, porque soy mal caminante.

– Digo, Sancho – respondió don Quijote –, que sea como tú quieras, que no me parece mal tu idea. Dentro de tres días te irás porque quiero que en este tiempo veas lo que hago y digo por mi dama.

– ¿Qué más tengo que ver – dijo Sancho – que lo que he visto?

– Todavía me falta – respondió don Quijote – romper los vestidos, esparcir las armas y darme de *calabazadas* por estas peñas, con otras cosas semejantes que te han de admirar.

– Por el amor de Dios – dijo Sancho –, que mire vuestra merced cómo se da esos golpes. Mi parecer es que, ya que a vuestra merced le parece que las calabazadas son aquí necesarias y que no se puede hacer esta obra sin ellas, se contentase con dárselas en el agua o en alguna cosa blanda como algodón, que yo diré a mi señora que se las daba en la punta de una peña durísima.

– Te agradezco tu buena intención, Sancho – respondió don Quijote –; pero quiero que sepas que todas estas cosas que hago no son burlas, sino que las hago muy de veras; porque de otra manera sería no cumplir las órdenes de caballería, que nos mandan no decir mentira alguna, y el hacer una cosa por otra es lo mismo que mentir. Así que

---

suplir, ocupar el lugar de otro que falta o hacer lo que otro no puede.
calabazada, golpe dado con la cabeza.

mis calabazadas han de ser verdaderas sin que lleven nada de mentira; y será necesario que me dejes lo que sea *menester* para curarme.

– Le ruego a vuestra merced – respondió Sancho – que considere que han pasado los tres días que me ha dado para que le vea las locuras que hace, y que ya las he visto todas, y le diré maravillas a mi señora; escriba la carta y mándeme con ella, que tengo ganas de volver pronto y sacar a vuestra merced de esta penitencia en la que le dejo.

– Bien dices – dijo el de la Triste Figura –; pero ¿qué haremos para escribir la carta?

– Y la cédula de los asnos – añadió Sancho.

– Todo irá junto – dijo don Quijote –; y ya que no hay papel sería bueno escribir en las hojas de los árboles como hacían los antiguos. Pero ya sé dónde escribirla: en el librillo de memoria que encontramos y tú la harás trasladar a papel en el primer lugar que halles, donde haya maestro de escuela de muchachos.

– ¿Qué se ha de hacer con la firma? – dijo Sancho.

– Nunca las cartas de Amadís se firmaron – respondió don Quijote.

– Está bien – dijo Sancho –, pero la cédula es necesario que esté firmada.

– La cédula irá en el mismo librillo, firmada; y cuando mi sobrina la vea la cumplirá sin dificultad. Y en la carta harás poner por firma: «Vuestro hasta la muerte, el Caballero de la Triste Figura». No importa que la carta vaya escrita por otro, porque Dulcinea no sabe leer ni escribir y nunca ha visto ninguna carta mía; en doce

---

sea menester, sea necesario.

años no la he visto ni cuatro veces, pues su padre Lorenzo Corchuelo y su madre la han criado con mucho *recato*.

– ¿Que la hija de Lorenzo Corchuelo es la señora Dulcinea del Toboso, llamada por otro nombre Aldonza Lorenzo?

– Esa es – dijo don Quijote –, y es la que merece ser señora de todo el mundo.

– Bien la conozco – dijo Sancho – ¡Qué voz tiene! Un día se puso en el *campanario* de la iglesia para llamar a unos *zagales* suyos, que estaban en un campo de su padre, y aunque estaban a más de media legua, la oyeron como si estuvieran junto a ella.

– Ya te he dicho muchas veces, Sancho – dijo don Quijote – que eres muy gran hablador, pero quiero que sepas que, por lo que yo quiero a Dulcinea, vale tanto como la más hermosa princesa de la tierra.

– Vuestra merced tiene razón – dijo Sancho. Escriba vuestra merced la carta que yo llevaré el libro bien guardado.

Don Quijote sacó el librillo y con mucho sosiego escribió la carta. Una vez acabada, llamó a Sancho y le dijo que se la quería leer por si se le perdía el libro por el camino.

– Léamela vuestra merced – dijo Sancho – que me gustará mucho oírla, pero pensar que la voy a aprender de memoria, es locura, porque a veces no me acuerdo ni de mi nombre.

– Escucha – dijo don Quijote.

---

recato, cuidado; retiro.
campanario, torre pequeña donde están colocadas las campanas de la iglesia.
zagal, muchacho, pastor joven.

«Soberana y *alta* señora: el herido de punta de ausencia, dulcísima Dulcinea del Toboso, te envía la salud que él no tiene. Si tu hermosura me desprecia, aunque yo sea muy *sufrido*, mal podré sostenerme en esta pena, que, además de ser fuerte, es muy duradera. Mi buen escudero Sancho te dará entera relación del modo en que por tu causa quedo. Si quieres ayudarme, tuyo soy; si no haz lo que te viniere en gusto; que con acabar mi vida habré satisfecho a tu crueldad y a mi deseo. Tuyo hasta la muerte, El Caballero de la Triste Figura».

–Esta carta es lo mejor que he oído – dijo Sancho –. Digo de verdad que no hay cosa que vuestra merced no sepa.

– Todo es necesario – respondió don Quijote – para el oficio que yo tengo.

– Ponga vuestra merced en esta otra hoja – dijo Sancho – la cédula de los tres pollinos, y fírmela con mucha claridad, para que cuando la vean la conozcan.

– Así lo haré – dijo don Quijote.

Y habiéndola escrito, se la leyó, y decía así:

«Mandará vuestra merced, por esta cédula, señora sobrina, dar a mi escudero Sancho Panza tres de los cinco *pollinos* que dejé en casa y que *están a cargo de* vuestra merced. Los cuales tres pollinos se los mando pagar por otros tantos aquí recibidos. Hecha en Sierra Morena, a veinte y dos de agosto de este presente año».

Sancho le pidió la bendición a su señor y, no sin muchas lágrimas de los dos, se despidió de él y subió sobre Rocinante.

---

alta, sentido figurado 'elevado', aplicado a personas importantes.
sufrido, con mucha capacidad para sufrir, tener esta capacidad.
pollino, asno, burro.
estar a cargo de, estar bajo el cuidado de.

No había andado cien pasos, cuando volvió y dijo:

– Señor, vuestra merced tiene razón: para que pueda afirmar sin cargo de conciencia que le he visto hacer locuras, será bien que haga siquiera una.

– ¿No te lo decía yo? – dijo don Quijote –. Espérate, Sancho, que en un momento las haré.

Sin más ni más dio dos *zapatetas* en el aire, la cabeza abajo y los pies en alto. Sancho se puso de nuevo en camino, contento de que podía jurar que su amo estaba loco.

---

sin más ni más, sin dar explicación alguna.
zapateta, salto acompañado de otro movimiento.

Preguntas

1. ¿En qué consistió la penitencia de don Quijote?

2. ¿Qué le aconseja Sancho y qué le responde a éste don Quijote?

3. ¿Quién es Dulcinea del Toboso?

4. ¿Qué le escribe don Quijote a Dulcinea en la carta?

5. ¿Por qué vuelve Sancho, una vez que había partido?

EL CURA Y EL BARBERO SACAN A SU
AMIGO DON QUIJOTE DE SIERRA MORENA

Sancho salió al camino real, y se fue en busca del camino del Toboso, y al otro día llegó a la venta donde había estado con don Quijote en el momento en que salieron de ella dos personas que le conocieron, y una dijo a la otra:

– Dígame, señor licenciado, aquél del caballo ¿no es Sancho Panza, el que salió, según el ama, con don Quijote sirviéndole como escudero?

– Sí es – dijo el licenciado –; y aquél es el caballo de nuestro don Quijote.

Eran el cura y el barbero de su mismo pueblo, que, cuando acabaron de conocer a Sancho y a Rocinante, le dijeron:

– Amigo Sancho Panza, ¿dónde quedó vuestro amo?

Sancho también los conoció, y determinó de ocultar el lugar y la manera en que quedaba don Quijote; les respondió que su amo quedaba ocupado en cierta parte y en cierta cosa que le era de mucha importancia, la cual él no podía descubrir de ninguna manera.

– No, no, – dijo el barbero –; Sancho Panza: si vos no nos decís dónde queda vuestro amo, pensaremos, como ya pensamos, que vos le habéis matado y robado, pues venís encima de su caballo.

– No hay para qué esas amenazas: yo no soy hombre que robe ni mate a nadie; a cada uno le mate su suerte, o Dios que le hizo: mi amo queda haciendo penitencia entre esas montañas.

Luego, sin parar, les contó cómo don Quijote quedaba, las aventuras que le habían sucedido con él; y cómo él

llevaba la carta a la señora Dulcinea del Toboso, que era la hija de Lorenzo Corchuelo, de la que su amo estaba enamorado.

Quedaron admirados los dos de lo que les contaba Sancho Panza, y aunque ya sabían la locura de don Quijote, siempre que la oían se admiraban de nuevo.

Le pidieron a Sancho que les enseñase la carta que llevaba. Él dijo que iba escrita en un libro de memoria, y que era orden de su señor que la hiciera escribir en papel; a lo cual dijo el cura que él la escribiría con muy buena letra.

Sancho empezó a buscar el libro, pero no lo podía encontrar porque se había quedado don Quijote con él, y ni don Quijote se lo había dado, ni Sancho se acordó de pedírselo.

Cuando Sancho vio que no lo encontraba, se llevó los dos *puños* a las barbas y se arrancó la mitad de ellas.

---

puño, mano cerrada.

El cura y el barbero al ver esto, le preguntaron qué le había sucedido.

– ¿Qué me ha de suceder? – respondió Sancho – sino que he perdido en un instante tres asnos cada uno como un castillo.

– ¿Cómo es eso? – replicó el barbero.

– He perdido el libro de memoria donde venía la carta para Dulcinea y la cédula por la que mi señor mandaba a su sobrina que me diera los tres pollinos. Y así les contó cómo había perdido el suyo.

El cura le consoló y le dijo que, cuando encontrara a su señor, él le haría otra cédula.

Con esto se consoló Sancho, y dijo que si eso era así no le daba mucha pena de la pérdida de la carta de Dulcinea, porque él la sabía casi de memoria.

– Lo que ahora hay que hacer – dijo el cura – es ver cómo sacar a vuestro amo de aquella penitencia inútil. Y para pensar esto y para comer, será bueno que entremos en la venta.

Sancho, acordándose de lo que le había sucedido en ella, dijo que entrasen ellos y que él esperaría allí fuera; pero que le sacasen allí algo de comer para él y para Rocinante. Ellos entraron y Sancho se quedó fuera, y el barbero, al poco rato, le sacó de comer.

Después, habiendo pensado entre los dos la manera de poder sacar de la Sierra a don Quijote, el cura encontró algo muy del gusto del caballero, y útil para lo que ellos querían: él se vestiría de doncella andante y el barbero haría lo posible por parecer el escudero y así irían donde estaba don Quijote. Fingiendo el cura ser una doncella afligida y necesitada de ayuda le pediría un favor, el cual él no podría dejar de concederle: que se fuese con ella a donde ella le guiase, para deshacerle una ofensa que un mal caballero le había hecho. Así le llevarían a su lugar, donde procurarían ver si tenía algún remedio su extraña locura.

No le pareció mal al barbero la idea del cura, sino tan bien que la pusieron por obra. Pidieron a la ventera ropas de mujer para el cura y algo para el barbero.

Apenas salieron de la venta, el cura pensó que hacía mal en vestirse de aquella manera, por no ser cosa propia de un cura el hacerlo. Se lo dijo al barbero y le propuso que cambiasen de traje. El barbero aceptó lo que el cura decía y éste le fue diciendo lo que tenía que hacer y las palabras que había de decir a don Quijote para obligarle a que dejase su penitencia.

Al otro día llegaron al lugar cerca de donde estaba don Quijote. Sancho se fue a buscar a su amo y dejó al cura y al barbero en un lugar por donde corría un tranquilo y pequeño arroyo, y al que daban sombra agradable y fresca algunos árboles. Todo hacía el sitio agradable y allí esperaron la vuelta de Sancho.

Estando allí, vieron venir hacia ellos dos viajeros perdidos en la Sierra: un hombre llamado Cardenio y una hermosa labradora llamada Dorotea. Después de saludarles cortésmente, se pusieron a hablar con ellos y el barbero les contó la causa por la que estaban allí y la extraña locura de don Quijote y cómo estaban esperando a su escudero que había ido a buscarle.

Estaban hablando de todo esto, cuando oyeron voces y conocieron que las daba Sancho Panza. Salieron a su encuentro y le preguntaron por don Quijote. Les dijo que había hallado a su amo amarillo y muerto de hambre, y que cuando le había dicho que la señora Dulcinea le mandaba que saliese de aquel lugar y se fuese al Toboso, donde le estaba esperando, había respondido que no pensaba aparecer ante ella hasta que no hubiese realizado hazañas dignas de su gracia; que por eso él, Sancho, les rogaba que hiciesen algo para sacar de allí a su amo. El cura le respondió que no tuviese pena, que ellos le sacarían

Contó luego el cura a Cardenio y a Dorotea lo que habían pensado para remedio de don Quijote, o por lo menos, para llevarle a su casa. Dorotea dijo que ella haría de doncella andante necesitada mejor que el barbero, y que tenía allí vestidos para hacerlo muy bien; que la dejasen representar todo aquello que fuera menester para llevar adelante su idea, porque ella había leído muchos libros de caballerías y conocía el estilo que tenían las doncellas necesitadas de ayuda cuando pedían favores a los caballeros andantes.

A todos les pareció muy bien la idea y a todos les contentó la mucha gracia de Dorotea, sobre todo cuando la vieron con sus vestidos, adornada de manera que parecía una rica y gran señora.

El que más se admiró fue Sancho quien pidió al cura que le dijese quién era aquella gran señora y qué buscaba por aquellos lugares.

– Esta señora – respondió el cura –, Sancho hermano, es la *sucesora* del gran imperio de Micomicón, la cual viene en busca de vuestro amo para que le repare una ofensa que un mal gigante le ha hecho; por la fama que de buen caballero vuestro amo tiene por todo el mundo, ha venido a buscarle de Guinea esta princesa. Se llama – continuó el cura – la princesa Micomicona, porque si su reino se llama Micomicón, claro está que ella se tiene que llamar así.

Entonces le dijeron a Sancho que los guiase al lugar en

---

sucesora, la que sigue.

donde don Quijote estaba, y le advirtieron que no dijese
que conocía al barbero, porque en no conocerlo estaba el
poder sacar de allí a su amo.

Habían andado un rato, cuando descubrieron a don
Quijote. En cuanto Dorotea lo vio y fue avisada por Sancho
de que aquél era don Quijote, fue a ponerse de rodillas
delante de él y le habló de esta manera:

– De aquí no me levantaré, ¡oh valeroso caballero!,
hasta que vuestra bondad me conceda un favor, el cual
resultará en honra de vuestra persona y en bien de la más
triste y ofendida doncella que el sol haya visto.

– No os responderé palabra, hermosa señora – respondió don Quijote –, ni oiré más cosas de vos, hasta que no os levantéis de tierra.

– No me levantaré, señor – respondió la doncella –, si primero no me es concedido por vuestra bondad lo que pido.

– Yo os lo concedo – respondió don Quijote –, si no es en daño de mi Rey, de mi patria o de aquella que tiene la llave de mi corazón y de mi libertad.

– No será en daño de lo que decís, mi buen señor – replicó la dolorosa doncella.

Sancho se acercó a su señor y le dijo al oído:

– Bien puede vuestra merced, señor, concederle el favor que pide: es sólo matar a un gigante, y ésta que lo pide es la princesa Micomicona, reina del gran reino de Micomicón.

– Sea quien fuere – respondió don Quijote –; que yo haré lo que estoy obligado y lo que me dice mi conciencia, conforme a lo que tengo por oficio. Y volviéndose a la doncella le dijo:

– Vuestra gran hermosura se levante, que yo le concedo el favor que quiera pedirme.

– Pues lo que pido es – dijo la doncella – que vuestra generosa persona se venga luego conmigo donde yo le llevare y me prometa que no se ha de detener en otra aventura hasta hacerme justicia de un traidor que, contra todo derecho divino y humano, me ha quitado mi reino.

– Digo que así lo concedo – respondió don Quijote –, y mandó a Sancho que ensillase a Rocinante y que le pusiese a él las armas.

Sancho tomó las armas, que estaban colgadas de un árbol, y en un momento armó a su señor, el cual, viéndose armado, dijo:

– Vamos de aquí, en nombre de Dios, a favorecer a esta gran señora.

El barbero estaba aún de rodillas, teniendo gran cuidado de ocultar la risa. Viendo que ya el favor estaba concedido, y que don Quijote se apresuraba para ir a cumplirlo, se levantó, tomó de la mano a su señora y la ayudó a subir sobre una mula; luego subió don Quijote sobre Rocinante y el barbero, sobre otra mula, quedándose Sancho a pie; y todos se pusieron en camino.

Preguntas

1. ¿A quién vio Sancho Panza al llegar a la venta?

2. ¿Qué les contó Sancho al cura y al barbero?

3. ¿Qué hicieron el cura y el barbero para sacar a don Quijote de Sierra Morena?

4. ¿Por qué no quería entrar Sancho en la venta?

5. ¿Por qué no quería ir don Quijote al Toboso?

6. ¿Qué le dijo Dorotea a don Quijote?

7. ¿Qué respondió éste?

BATALLA DE DON QUIJOTE
CONTRA UNOS *CUEROS* DE *VINO TINTO*

Cardenio y el cura habían estado viéndolo todo por entre unas ramas y no sabían qué hacer para juntarse con sus compañeros; pero el cura, que era hombre de imaginación, dijo lo que iban a hacer.

Y fue que se pusieron a la salida de la Sierra y, cuando salió de ella don Quijote con sus compañeros, el cura se puso a mirarlo con mucha atención, y al fin se fue hacia él con los brazos abiertos y diciendo a grandes voces:

– Para bien sea hallado el espejo de la caballería, mi buen paisano don Quijote de la Mancha, el amparo y remedio de los necesitados, el mejor de los caballeros andantes. Diciendo esto, tenía abrazado a don Quijote por la rodilla de la pierna izquierda; el cual, maravillado de lo que veía y oía decir y hacer a aquel hombre, se puso a mirarle con atención. Al fin le reconoció y quedó como espantado de verle. Quiso bajarse del caballo, pero el cura no lo consintió, por lo cual don Quijote decía:

– Déjeme vuestra merced, señor licenciado; que no es razón que yo vaya a caballo y tan respetable persona como vuestra merced vaya a pie.

– Esto no lo consentiré yo de ninguna manera – dijo el

cuero

---

vino tinto, vino rojo.

cura –; vaya vuestra merced a caballo, pues estando a caballo acaba las mayores aventuras que se han visto en nuestro tiempo; a mí me bastará subir en una de las mulas de estos señores que con vuestras mercedes caminan.

Don Quijote le dijo a la doncella:

– Señora mía, guíe vuestra hermosura por donde más gusto le diere.

– ¿Hacia qué reino quiere guiar vuestra merced? Es acaso hacia el de Micomicón? Que sí debe ser, o yo sé poco de reinos.

Ella respondió:

– Sí, señor; hacia ese reino es mi camino.

– Si es así – dijo el cura –, por la mitad de mi pueblo hemos de pasar, y allí tomará vuestra merced el camino de *Cartagena*, donde se podrá embarcar; y si hay viento favorable y mar tranquilo, en poco menos de nueve años podrá estar cerca del reino de vuestra grandeza.

– Vuestra merced se engaña, señor mío – dijo ella –, porque no hace dos años que yo salí de mi reino y nunca tuve buen tiempo, pero aun así he llegado a ver lo que más deseaba, al señor don Quijote de la Mancha, cuyas hazañas llegaron a mis oídos en cuanto puse los pies en España.

– No más, cesen mis alabanzas – dijo don Quijote –, porque soy enemigo de todo género de ellas y semejantes conversaciones ofenden mis orejas.

Iban hablando, cuando, de repente, vieron venir por el camino a un hombre sobre un asno y cuando llegó cerca de ellos les pareció que era *gitano*; pero Sancho Panza, que

---

Cartagena, ver mapa.

gitano, individuo que pertenece a cierto pueblo esparcido por el mundo.

98

por todas partes por donde veía asnos, creía ver el suyo, conoció que el hombre era Ginés de Pasamonte y a grandes voces dijo:

– ¡Ah Ginesillo! ¡Suelta mi vida, deja mi asno! ¡Huye y deja lo que no es tuyo!

Ginés, al oír su nombre, saltó al suelo y desapareció de delante de todos en un momento. Sancho se acercó a donde estaba su asno y abrazándole le dijo:

– ¿Cómo has estado, bien mío, compañero mío?

Y diciendo esto, le besaba y le abrazaba como si fuera una persona. Y el asno le dejaba hacer, sin responderle palabra alguna. Llegaron todos y se alegraron con Sancho, porque éste había hallado a su asno, especialmente don Quijote, el cual le dijo que no por eso *anulaba* la cédula de los tres pollinos. Sancho se lo agradeció mucho.

Al otro día llegaron a la venta, espanto de Sancho, y aunque él hubiera querido no entrar, tuvo que hacerlo.

La ventera y el ventero, que vieron venir a don Quijote y a Sancho, salieron a recibirlos, dando señales de mucha alegría. Don Quijote pidió que le preparasen un lecho y se

---

anular, dejar sin efecto una cosa; aquí, la cédula.

acostó, porque venía muy cansado y falto de sueño. El cura pidió que les preparasen de comer lo que hubiera en la venta, y el ventero, con la esperanza del pago, les preparó una buena comida. Mientras ellos comían, don Quijote estaba durmiendo, pues no quisieron despertarle, pensando que le haría mejor el descanso que la comida.

Hablaron, entre otras cosas, de la extraña locura de don Quijote y, cuando Sancho no estaba allí, la ventera les contó lo que le habían hecho con la manta.

Estaban hablando de todo esto, cuando del lugar donde reposaba don Quijote salió Sancho diciendo a grandes voces:

– Acudid, señores, pronto y ayuda a mi señor, que anda envuelto en la más reñida batalla que mis ojos han visto; ha dado tal cuchillada al gigante enemigo de la señora princesa que le ha partido la cabeza al medio.

– ¿Qué dices, hermano? – dijo el cura – ¿Cómo puede ser eso estando el gigante a más de dos mil leguas de aquí?

En esto oyeron gran ruido en el aposento y que don Quijote decía a voces:

– ¡Detente que aquí te tengo, y no te ha de valer tu *cimitarra*!

Y parecía que daba grandes cuchilladas en las paredes. Y Sancho dijo:

– No tienen que pararse a escuchar, sino entrar y acabar con la batalla y ayudar a mi amo, porque, sin duda alguna, el gigante está ya muerto, y dando cuenta a Dios de su

cimitarra

bonete

caldero

pasada mala vida; que yo vi correr la sangre por el suelo y la cabeza cortada y caída a un lado, que es tan grande como un cuero de vino.

Al oír esto dijo el ventero:

– Ese don Quijote o don diablo ha dado alguna cuchillada en alguno de los cueros de vino tinto que en su aposento estaban llenos, y el vino derramado es lo que le parece sangre a este buen hombre.

Se fue al aposento, y todos detrás de él, y hallaron a don Quijote en el más extraño traje del mundo. Estaba en camisa, las piernas eran muy largas y flacas y llenas de *vello* y nada limpias; tenía en la cabeza un *bonete* colorado y sucio, que era del ventero; en el brazo izquierdo tenía envuelta la manta de la cama; en la mano derecha tenía la espada, con la cual daba cuchilladas a todas partes, diciendo palabras como si verdaderamente estuviera peleando con algún gigante. Y es lo bueno que no tenía los ojos abiertos, porque estaba durmiendo; que fue tan intensa la imaginación de la aventura que iba a acometer, que le hizo soñar que ya había llegado al reino de Micomicón. Había dado tantas cuchilladas a los cueros, creyendo que era el gigante, que todo el aposento estaba lleno de vino. Lo cual visto por el ventero, comenzó a darle golpes. Con todo, el pobre caballero no se despertó, hasta que el

---

vello, pelos cortos y finos que cubren algunas partes del cuerpo de las personas.

barbero trajo un *caldero* de agua fría y se lo echó encima.

Sancho andaba buscando la cabeza del gigante por el suelo, y como no la hallaba, dijo:

– Ya sé que todo lo de esta casa es encantamiento; ahora no aparece esta cabeza, que vi cortar con mis ojos, y la sangre corría del cuerpo como de una fuente.

– ¿Qué sangre ni qué fuente dices, enemigo de Dios? –

dijo el ventero – ¿No ves que la sangre y la fuente no son otra cosa que estos cueros que están aquí llenos de cuchilladas?

El cura había agarrado las manos a don Quijote, el cual, creyendo que ya había acabado la aventura y que se hallaba delante de la princesa Micomicoma, se puso de rodillas y le dijo:

– Bien puede vuestra hermosura, señora, vivir segura de que ya no le podrá hacer mal esta mal nacida criatura; yo soy libre de la palabra que os di, pues con la ayuda del cielo y el favor de aquélla por quien yo vivo y respiro, la he cumplido.

– ¿No lo dije yo? – dijo, oyendo esto, Sancho.

¿Quién no había de reír con los disparates de uno y otro? Todos reían menos el ventero, pero el cura lo calmó, y llevó a don Quijote a la cama, el cual se quedó dormido. Dorotea consoló a Sancho, el cual aseguró a la princesa que él había visto la cabeza del gigante por el suelo y que, si no aparecía, era porque todo lo que pasaba en aquella casa era cosa de encantamiento, como él lo había probado otra vez que había estado en ella.

Preguntas

1. ¿Qué le dijo el cura a don Quijote?

2. ¿Qué le dijo Sancho a Ginés y qué hizo éste?

3. ¿Qué le dijo Sancho a su asno?

4. ¿Qué sucedió en la venta?

5. Describir la lucha de don Quijote con los cueros de vino.

6. ¿Qué le dijo don Quijote a Dorotea después de la batalla?

7. ¿Qué le dijo Sancho a Dorotea?

EL ENCANTAMIENTO DE DON QUIJOTE Y SU VUELTA A LA ALDEA, CON LO QUE DA FIN LA PRIMERA PARTE DE LA HISTORIA DEL HIDALGO

Hacía dos días que estaban en la venta y, pareciéndoles que era el momento de partir, dieron orden para que sin el trabajo de ir Dorotea con don Quijote a su pueblo, pudiesen el cura y el barbero llevárselo y procurar la curación de su locura en su tierra.

Se pusieron de acuerdo con un hombre que llevaba un carro de bueyes y que pasaba por allí, para que lo llevase de este forma: hicieron como una *jaula* de palos en la que pudiese ir bien don Quijote, y luego todos se cubrieron los rostros y se vistieron unos de una manera y otros de otra, de modo que a don Quijote le pareciese que era otra gente distinta a la que antes había visto. Hecho esto, con grandísimo silencio, entraron donde él estaba durmiendo. Se acercaron a él y, cogiéndole fuertemente, le ataron las manos y los pies, de modo que cuando despertó asustado, no pudo moverse ni hacer otra cosa que admirarse de ver delante de él a tan extrañas figuras. Creyó que todas ellas eran *fantasmas* del castillo, y que, sin duda alguna, él estaba encantado, pues no se podía mover ni

jaula   fantasma

105

defender. Sancho conoció quiénes eran aquellas figuras, pero no abrió la boca, hasta ver *en qué paraba* todo aquello.

Llevaron la jaula al aposento de don Quijote, le encerraron en ella y luego le tomaron en hombros, y al salir del aposento, se oyó una voz que causaba temor, y fue tanto como supo hacerlo el barbero, que decía:

– ¡Oh Caballero de la Triste Figura! No te dé pena la forma en que vas, porque así conviene para acabar más pronto la aventura en que tu gran valor te puso.

Don Quijote quedó consolado y creyendo lo que le decían, alzó la voz, y dando un gran suspiro, dijo:

– ¡Oh, tú, que aunque no sé quién eres me has prometido tanto bien! Te ruego que le pidas de mi parte al sabio encantador que mis cosas tiene a cargo, que no me deje morir en esta *prisión* donde ahora me llevan.

Cuando don Quijote se vio encima del carro dijo:

– He leído muchas historias de caballeros andantes; pero jamás he leído, ni visto, ni oído que a los caballeros encantados los lleven de esta manera, porque siempre los suelen llevar por los aires con extraña ligereza, encerrados en alguna obscura nube o en algún carro de fuego. Que me lleven a mí ahora en un carro de bueyes, me pone en confusión. Pero quizá la caballería y los encantos de estos nuestros tiempos deben seguir otro camino distinto al de los antiguos.

Antes de que se moviese el carro, llegaron la ventera y su hija a despedirse de don Quijote, fingiendo que lloraban de dolor por la desgracia del caballero.

Don Quijote les dijo:

– No lloréis, mis buenas señoras, que todas estas desgra-

---

en qué paraba, cómo terminaba.
prisión, cárcel (fig.)

cias sufren los caballeros andantes; y si no me sucedieran estas cosas no *me tendría* yo *por* famoso caballero. A los caballeros de poco nombre y fama nunca les suceden semejantes casos, porque no hay en el mundo quien se acuerde de ellos, pero a los valerosos, sí.

Subió el cura a su caballo, y también su amigo el barbero y se pusieron a caminar tras el carro con el resto de la compañía. Don Quijote iba sentado en la jaula, con las manos atadas, y con tanto silencio y tanta paciencia como si no fuera hombre de carne y hueso, sino estatua de piedra.

Despacio y en silencio caminaron dos leguas, hasta llegar a un valle tranquilo y verde donde se detuvieron para reposar y para comer.

Soltaron los bueyes del carro y los dejaron andar a su gusto por aquel verde y apacible sitio. Sancho rogó al

me tendría por, me consideraría.

cura que permitiese a su señor salir de la jaula un rato porque si no le dejaba, no iría tan limpia aquella prisión como se debía a tal caballero.

El cura dijo que haría de muy buena gana lo que le pedía, pero que temía que, viéndose su señor en libertad, pudiera irse donde nadie le viese jamás. Pero si me promete – continuó el cura – como caballero que no se apartará de nosotros, le dejaré salir un rato de la jaula.

– Lo prometo – respondió don Quijote, que todo lo estaba escuchando –; además, el que está encantado, como yo, no tiene libertad para hacer de su persona lo que quisiere, porque el que le encantó puede hacer que no se mueva de un lugar en tres siglos; y si huye le hará volver por los aires.

El cura lo sacó de la jaula y don Quijote se alegró mucho; se fue a donde estaba Rocinante y le dijo:

– Aún espero en Dios y en su bendita Madre, flor y espejo de caballos, que pronto nos veremos los dos como deseamos: tú con tu señor encima y yo ejerciendo el oficio para el que Dios me trajo al mundo.

Dicho esto, se apartó don Quijote y al rato volvió.

Se sentaron a la sombra de unos árboles y comieron todos en paz y compañía.

Después se pusieron en camino y, a los siete días, llegaron a la aldea de don Quijote, a donde entraron a mitad del día, que era domingo, y la gente estaba toda en la plaza, por la mitad de la cual atravesó el carro de don Quijote. Acudieron todos a ver lo que en el carro venía, y cuando conocieron a su vecino quedaron maravillados. Un muchacho fue corriendo a dar la noticia al ama y a la sobrina de que su señor y tío venía flaco y amarillo sobre un carro de bueyes.

Fue cosa de lástima oír los gritos de las dos pobres se-

ñoras y las maldiciones que echaron a los libros de caballerías, todo lo cual aumentó cuando vieron entrar a don Quijote por sus puertas.

A las noticias de la venida de don Quijote, acudió la mujer de Sancho Panza, que ya sabía que su marido se había ido con don Quijote a servirle como escudero, y así como vio a Sancho, lo primero que le preguntó fue que si venía bueno el asno. Sancho respondió que venía mejor que su amo.

– Gracias sean dadas a Dios – dijo ella –, que tanto bien me ha hecho; pero contadme ahora, amigo: ¿qué bien habéis sacado por ser escudero? ¿Qué me traéis a mi? ¿Qué zapatos traéis a vuestros hijos?

– No traigo nada de esto – dijo Sancho –, mujer mía, aunque sí otras cosas de más consideración.

– De eso recibo yo mucho gusto – respondió la mujer –; mostradme esas cosas para que se me alegre el corazón, que tan triste ha estado en todos los siglos de vuestra ausencia.

– En casa os las mostraré, mujer – dijo Sancho –, y por ahora estad contenta; que si Dios quiere y salimos otra vez a buscar aventuras, vos me veréis pronto gobernador de una ínsula, y no de cualquiera, sino de la mejor que pueda hallarse.

– Quiéralo así el cielo, marido mío; que bien lo necesitamos. Mas decidme: ¿qué es eso de ínsulas, que no lo entiendo?

– *No es la miel para la boca del asno* – respondió Sancho –. A su tiempo lo verás. Ahora sólo te sé decir que no hay cosa mejor en el mundo que ser un hombre honrado escudero de un caballero andante que anda buscando aventuras.

Así hablaban Sancho y su mujer mientras el ama y la sobrina recibieron a don Quijote y le llevaron a su antiguo aposento y le pusieron en su antigua cama. Él las miraba y no acababa de entender en qué parte estaba. El cura le encargó a la sobrina que cuidase muy bien a su tío y que estuviese con cuidado de que no se les escapase otra vez. Le contó también todo lo que había sido necesario hacer para llevarle a su casa. Al oírlo el ama y la sobrina, volvieron a llorar a grandes voces y repitieron las maldiciones contra los libros de caballerías, y pidieron al cielo que castigase a los autores de tantas mentiras y locuras. Finalmente se callaron, pero se quedaron con miedo de que se quedarían otra vez sin su amo y tío en el mismo momento en que don Quijote tuviese alguna mejoría, y así fue como ellas se lo imaginaron.

---

no es la miel para la boca del asno, refrán que se dice cuando alguien no sabe o no puede apreciar lo bueno de una cosa o de una situación.

Preguntas

1. ¿Qué hicieron el cura y el barbero con don Quijote?

2. ¿Qué le respondió don Quijote al barbero?

3. ¿Qué dijo don Quijote cuando se vio sobre el carro?

4. ¿Cómo iba don Quijote?

5. ¿Cuándo llegaron al pueblo y qué sucedió a su llegada?

6. ¿Qué hicieron el ama y la sobrina cuando vieron llegar a don Quijote?

7. ¿Qué le dijo Teresa Panza a su marido?

8. ¿Qué pensaron la sobrina y el ama?

9. ¿Volvió a marcharse don Quijote a buscar aventuras?

NOTAS

Libros de caballerías, libros en los que se cuenta lo que hacían los *caballeros andantes*, que iban por el mundo buscando sucesos extraordinarios en los que mostrar su valor.

Bucéfalo, cabeza de buey, nombre del caballo de *Alejandro Magno*, rey de Macedonia (356-323 a.d.J.C.).

Babieca, nombre del caballo de Rodrigo Díaz de Vivar, llamado el *Cid Campeador* (1043-1099). El Cid pasó su vida luchando contra los moros, quienes le llamaron Cid (= señor), y al servicio del rey de Castilla.

Amadís de Gaula, personaje principal del libro del mismo nombre. Este libro es uno de los más célebres de entre los de caballerías y Amadís es el caballero perfecto y amante fiel.

Tirante el Blanco, novela de caballerías escrita en catalán (1490) por Martorell y por Juan de Galba.

Frestón, Fristón, sabio encantador que se supone había escrito el libro de caballerías titulado *Don Belianís de Grecia*.

Briareo, uno de los gigantes que quiso luchar contra Júpiter; tenía, según la mitología, cien brazos.

vos, forma de tratamiento, 1: de respeto, usado en lugar de 'usted'. 2: tratamiento que dan los superiores a los inferiores. Estos son usos de la lengua antigua.

Santa Hermandad, tribunal de aquella época que se ocupaba de juzgar los crímenes cometidos fuera de los lugares habitados.

Peña Pobre o Peña del *Ermitaño*, – hombre que vive solo –, morada o vivienda de Andalod situada en una isla imaginaria. En ella encuentra Amadís al ermitaño cuando se retiró a la Peña Pobre para hacer penitencia de amor.

INNOCENT VIRGIN, WILD SURRENDER

BY

ANNE MATHER

MILLS &
BOON®

First published in Great Britain 2010
Harlequin Mills & Boon Limited,
Eton House, 18-24 Paradise Road, Richmond, Surrey TW9 1SR

© Anne Mather 2010

ISBN: 978 0 263 87867 7

Harlequin Mills & Boon policy is to use papers that are natural, renewable and recyclable products and made from wood grown in sustainable forests. The logging and manufacturing process conform to the legal environmental regulations of the country of origin.

Printed and bound in Spain
by Litografia Rosés, S.A., Barcelona

INNOCENT VIRGIN, WILD SURRENDER

CHAPTER ONE

'THIS yo' first trip to St Antoine?'

Rachel dragged her eyes away from the exotic sight of hibiscus growing wild beside the airport buildings to give the taxi driver a slightly dazed look.

'What? Oh—oh, yes. It's my first visit to the Caribbean,' she admitted ruefully. 'I can hardly believe I'm here.'

And wasn't that the truth? she conceded silently. A week ago she'd had no intention of taking an unplanned break in these semi-tropical surroundings. But that had been before her father broke the news that her mother had left him. Sara Claiborne had apparently abandoned her home and her husband to fly out to the small island of St Antoine to visit a man she'd known many years ago.

'Did she say when she was coming back?'

Rachel's first thought had been a practical one, but her father had been uncharacteristically morose.

'Don't you mean *if* she's coming back?' he'd mumbled bitterly. 'And if she doesn't I don't know what I'm going to do.'

Rachel had felt out of her depth. Although she'd always believed her parents' marriage was rock-solid, occasionally she'd sensed a certain ambivalence in their treatment of each other. On top of which, her mother's attitude towards her had generally made her feel that it wasn't her problem. And if that was a little hard to take at times, she'd assumed it was simply a case of their different attitudes towards life.

Still, she had believed that Sara and Ralph Claiborne loved one another, and that, unlike lots of their friends and neighbours, their marriage was unlikely to be torn apart by rows or infidelity.

But what did she know, really? At age thirty she was still unmarried and a virgin, so any judgements she made were hardly the result of experience.

'So who is this man?' she'd asked, but her father had been carefully reticent on that point.

'His name's Matthew Brody,' had been all he'd say in response. 'He's someone she knew—years ago, as I say.' He'd paused, before exploding his next bombshell. 'I want you to go after her, Rachel. I want you to bring her home.'

Rachel had stared at him disbelievingly. 'Me?' she'd exclaimed ungrammatically. 'Why can't you go after her yourself?'

'Because I can't.' Ralph Claiborne had regarded her from beneath lowered lids. 'I just can't do it. Surely you can understand that, Rachel? What would I do if she turned me away?'

The same as me, I suppose, thought Rachel unhappily, but she could see where this was going. Whoever this man was, her father saw him as a threat to their relationship—and how could she refuse to help him when there was evidently so much at stake?

It troubled her that her mother had chosen to meet this man on an island in the Caribbean. But when she'd asked her father about this, he'd explained that Matthew Brody lived on St Antoine. It troubled her, too, that she'd never sensed the distance that must have been growing between her parents for such a potentially devastating situation to develop.

But then, she'd never been particularly close to her mother. They didn't share the same interests or like the same things. It was different with her father, but perhaps she hadn't expected as much from him.

Rachel sighed as she remembered the rest of the conversation. Her own pleas that she couldn't just walk out on her job at the local newspaper had fallen on stony ground.

'I'll have a word with Don,' said her father at once. 'I'll explain that Sara needs a break and, as I can't leave the office right now, I've asked you to take my place. He can't object to you taking a couple of weeks' unpaid holiday. Not after you've kept going when half his staff have been down with flu.'

'I've been lucky,' Rachel had protested, but it had been no use.

She knew that because Don Graham, the editor at the paper, and her father had gone to school together. Ralph Claiborne considered he was responsible for her getting a job there in the first place. And perhaps he was, although Rachel preferred not to believe it. She had been straight out of college, it was true, but with a good degree in English, and computer skills, she liked to think she'd got the job on her own merits.

Needless to say her father had been as good as his word. The following morning Don Graham had called her into his office and told her that another girl would be taking over her duties in the advertising department from now on.

'Your father says your mother hasn't been well all winter,' he'd said, and Rachel had felt her face burning. 'I'm giving you a couple of weeks' compassionate leave. Just don't make a habit of it, you hear?'

So here she was, over three thousand miles from home, without the faintest notion of how she was going to handle the situation. She was still sure her mother loved her father, but she didn't know how that love would fare in the face of another attachment. And who was this other attachment— this Matthew Brody? And why did Rachel feel such a sense of foreboding at the prospect of seeing her mother again?

'You here for a holiday?'

The taxi driver was speaking again, and Rachel knew he was only trying to be friendly. But, goodness, how could she answer that question when what she felt was that she was on the edge of a precipice with no practical means of getting down?

'Um—a holiday?' She licked her dry lips. 'Yes, I suppose so.'

It wasn't the right answer. She could see that in the dark eyes that met hers in the rearview mirror. The man's expression was both curious and wary, and she guessed he was wondering what kind of kook he was driving.

To distract herself, she turned her attention back to the view. Beyond the environs of the small inter-island airport, the road was narrow and unpaved. But the sight of the ocean creaming onto almost white sands below the thick grasses that grew on the clifftop was a definite lift to her spirits. Whatever else, she was being given a totally new—totally unexpected—experience, and she should try and get as much out of it as she could.

She'd never even heard of St Antoine before her father mentioned it to her. It was one of a small group of islands off the coast of Jamaica. Near the Caymans, but not part of them. A handful of mountains and reefs and jewel-bright vegetation where, according to her father, the only industries were a little sugar cane and coffee and, of course, tourism.

'You stayin' long?'

'Two weeks.'

At least Rachel could be honest about that. Well, providing her mother didn't send her packing the minute she saw her. That was always a possibility, and Rachel didn't know if she had a strong enough motivation to stay on under those circumstances.

Though she could, she reminded herself consideringly. Her father had booked her into St Antoine's only hotel and there was no reason why she should waste the reservation.

She'd been lucky to get it, and only because someone else had cancelled at the last moment.

'You keen on water sports, miss?'

The driver was determined to learn more about her, and Rachel pulled a wry face.

'I like swimming,' she admitted, not sure what else he was referring to. Unless it was snorkelling. She had tried that once in Spain.

'Not much else to do on St Antoine,' he persisted. 'We got no movie theatres or nightclubs. Not a lot of call for stuff like that.'

'I would suppose not,' murmured Rachel, a cynical smile pulling down the corners of her mouth.

Well, he'd lasted a full ten minutes before making an oblique reference to her appearance. She doubted the elderly taxi driver was interested in her, but the fact remained he had already associated her with the kind of nightlife more readily found in Havana or Kingston.

She grimaced. A lifetime—an adult lifetime, anyway—of parrying personal comments and sexual innuendo had taught her to ignore all references to her face and figure. So she was almost six feet tall, blonde, with full breasts and long legs? But what of it? She didn't like the way she looked or the way men looked at her. Which was probably why she was still single, and likely to remain so for the foreseeable future.

When she was younger, she'd used to worry about her height and her appearance. She'd used to wish she was shorter, smaller, darker. More like her mother. Anything to avoid standing out in a crowd of girls her own age.

But her years at college had convinced her that boys never looked beyond the obvious. She was a blonde, therefore she was a bimbo. With an IQ no bigger than her bust size.

'Is it far to town?' she asked, leaning forward, deciding to take advantage of the man's garrulousness to ask some questions of her own.

'Not far,' he replied, swinging out to pass a mule-drawn cart. It was loaded with banana plants that hung precariously over its sides. He beeped his horn and the mule jerked nervously.

'You stayin' at the Tamarisk, yeah?'

'That's right.' Rachel was grateful to discuss her destination. 'It's just a small hotel, I believe. I suppose it will be busy at this time of the year?'

'Oh, sure.' The man nodded expansively, turning the wheel of the car. The little statue of the Madonna that was suspended above his mirror swung in sympathy. 'Janu'ry, Febru'ry—they's our busiest months. 'Course, we do get visitors in summer, but when it's winter in the UK and the United States, that's when we get most tourists.' He paused. 'Like yourself.'

'Mmm.'

Rachel absorbed this, but she didn't comment. She was wondering how she could get around to mentioning Matthew Brody's name. It was a small island, and a small population. Surely it wasn't beyond the realms of possibility that he might have heard of the man?

The road that had been riding along the cliff now swung inland, and Rachel stared at the thickly wooded vegetation covering the land that rose on the right. Trees and shrubs, ferns and bushes, all exploding with colour. Even in the late afternoon, the brilliance of the sunlight was dazzling.

They were nearing the small town of St Antoine, she realised. Outlying dwellings, some of them with a plot of land given over to either cattle or crops, bordered the road, and presently an occasional store boasted signs that read 'Fresh Sandwiches' or 'Home-made Ice-cream'.

Now the road was divided into two lanes by a belt of palm trees. Rachel could see shops and houses with bougainvillea dripping from every roof and balcony. She glimpsed frangipani and oleander behind iron railings, and lots of West Indian faces peering at her as the taxi drove by.

'Um—I don't suppose you know a man called Brody?' she ventured at last, realising she couldn't afford to waste any more time. They'd be at the hotel soon and any chance would be lost.

'You mean Jacob Brody?' The taxi driver didn't wait for her to correct him before going on. 'Sure, everyone knows Jacob Brody. Seein' as how he and his son own most of the island.'

Rachel's eyes widened. Her father had told her nothing about the Brodys at all. Somehow she'd got the impression that this man—Matthew Brody—was some kind of playboy. That he and her mother must have had an affair.

'I—'

She'd been about to ask if Matthew Brody was related to Jacob when the taxi turned between wrought-iron gates. Ahead, she could see what she assumed was the Tamarisk Hotel. A two-storeyed stucco-painted structure, with a fountain playing on the forecourt out front.

'This is it.'

Her driver, a barrel-chested man, with a luxuriant moustache and cornrows, thrust open his door and got out. Then, after swinging the passenger door open for Rachel, he walked round to the rear of the vehicle to haul her suitcase out of the boot.

Rachel followed him and thrust a handful of dollars into his palm. She never knew how much to tip people, but judging by the man's expression she'd overdone it this time.

Oh, well…

'You know the Brodys?' the man asked, evidently associating her generosity with the man he'd spoken of, but Rachel shook her head.

'No,' she said, not wanting to get into a discussion. 'I can manage,' she added, when he would have carried her suitcase into the hotel. She pulled up the handle on the case to demonstrate, and then towed it after her as she walked away. 'Thank you.'

'My pleasure.' The driver stuffed the bills into his pocket. 'Yo' want anything else while you're here, yo' just let Aaron know.' He nodded towards the hotel. 'They got my number.'

Rachel doubted she'd take him up on it, but she cast him a polite smile over her shoulder. However, privately she was thinking that she'd have to be more diligent with her cash. She couldn't afford to go throwing money around, whatever happened here.

Two shallow steps that stretched along the front of the building led up to a wide verandah. Cane chairs and tables sheltered beneath the shadow of an awning, and tall columns were wound about with flowering vines. She entered into a marble-tiled foyer, where more flowers rioted from tubs and urns.

The reception desk was immediately ahead of her, but, glancing up, she saw that the second-floor rooms all opened onto a curving balcony that swept around the upper floor. The ceiling of the reception area was open to an airy atrium, and although there didn't appear to be a lift a staircase hugged the outer wall.

A pretty West Indian girl was in charge of the reception desk, and as there were few people about at the moment she watched Rachel's approach with a critical eye. Rachel doubted there was any aspect of her appearance that had gone unnoticed, but she was used to ignoring that kind of attention.

'Hi, there, welcome to the Tamarisk,' the girl said, her smile as practised as her manner. 'You have a reservation, Ms—er—'

'Claiborne,' said Rachel pleasantly. 'Yes, it was just made a few days ago.'

'Of course.'

The girl's voice had the slow, attractive drawl of the islands that Rachel had already noticed at the airport. And while she brought up Rachel's booking on the computer, Rachel took the time to examine her surroundings more fully.

The hotel was small, it was true, but it was very attractive. Not least because of the white stone pillars that supported the balcony, and the airy brightness of its public rooms. There was a pleasant scent of spices and sweetness. The air outside had been close and humid, but here the layout of the foyer allowed a cross breeze that cooled her skin.

'Here we are, Ms Claiborne.'

The girl—her name-tag read Rosa—had evidently found what she was looking for. Rescuing a pen from the drawer in front of her, she pushed a registration form towards Rachel.

'If you just fill this in,' she said, her dark eyes assessing. 'Then I'll get Toby to show you to your room.'

'Thanks.'

Rachel rested the backpack she'd carried instead of a handbag on the counter and picked up the pen. This part was familiar to her. She'd stayed in plenty of hotels before, albeit not in such exotic surroundings. She couldn't suppress a momentary twinge of excitement. Whatever else, this was an experience she wouldn't forget.

She was checking to see that she'd supplied all the necessary information when she became aware of a sudden quickening in the air. Someone else had entered the foyer, and judging by the way the receptionist straightened her spine and adjusted her cleavage it was someone she wanted to impress.

A man, then, thought Rachel cynically. She doubted Rosa would make such an effort for a member of her own sex. Unable to resist, she peeked beneath her arm and saw tan loafers and taut muscular calves clad in black denim.

Definitely a man, she conceded, straightening. Women were such clichés. Didn't they realise their reactions were so obvious to a man?

'Hi, Matt.'

Matt!

Was that a coincidence? Rachel couldn't help herself. She swung round to see who had garnered so much excitement in the building. And found herself confronted by a tall dark man, with a lean muscular frame and broad shoulders.

She supposed he was attractive in a hard athletic sort of way. She was trying to be detached about it, but for once it wasn't easy. The short-sleeved black shirt that matched his pants was coming loose from his waistband in places. So sexy. And she could see the dusky tattoo of some predatory winged beast etched around his upper arm.

He was olive-skinned and clean-shaven, although she doubted he would ever be able to erase the dark shadow on his jawline. His hair was thick and straight, and just a little too long for her liking. But he evidently ticked all the boxes so far as Rosa was concerned.

'Hey, Mr Brody's been phoning here all day, looking for you,' she said, her expression undeniably seductive. 'He's definitely on your case. I'd give him a ring, if I was you.'

'Would you, now?'

Rachel's stomach plunged. Despite being convinced now that this was the man she was looking for, his voice caused a primal leap of her senses. It was deep, dark, like black molasses soaked in treacle. Well, that was probably a contradiction, but she couldn't deny its sensual appeal.

Which bothered her quite a bit. She wasn't used to having this kind of response to a man—any man. And if this was the man her mother had apparently flown out here to meet, it was all the more disturbing.

But it couldn't be this man. Surely. He had to be at least ten years younger than Sara Claiborne and a sexy hunk besides. If he was, and her mother had succeeded in attracting his attention, she couldn't help acknowledging that Ralph Claiborne simply wasn't in his league.

She wondered what he was doing here. Was her mother

staying here, too? At this hotel? She could hardly ask him. She simply wasn't capable of making such a leap. No, somehow she was going to have to get to know this man. Would it be beyond her capabilities to gain his trust?

Her lips compressed resignedly.

Probably.

CHAPTER TWO

THE man had noticed her now.

Well, he could hardly help it, she supposed, seeing as how she was standing staring at him as if she'd never seen a man before. And because of this she felt hot colour filling her cheeks. Although she turned quickly back to the desk, she was sure he must have seen it.

Rosa was completing her reservation with one eye on what she was doing and the other on the man who was approaching the desk. She pulled open another drawer and extracted a small folder containing a key card. Then, picking up the bell beside her, she gave it a peremptory ring.

'Are you checking in?'

Rachel started. The molasses-dark voice was speaking to her now, and she swallowed convulsively before turning in his direction.

'I—oh, yes.' What it had to do with him she couldn't imagine, but she wasn't about to look a gift horse in the mouth. She licked her lips. 'Are you?'

His smile was wide, but faintly ironic, and the explanation was clear when Rosa piped up again.

'Mr Brody owns the hotel,' she said, her voice full of amused disdain. Then, as a young West Indian man appeared, she held out the key card towards him. 'Toby, will show you to your room, Ms Claiborne.' Another practised smile. 'I hope you enjoy your stay.'

'Claiborne?'

Before Rachel could move away, the man—Matt Brody—spoke. He'd come to stand beside her at the reception desk, and she was suddenly aware of the heat of his body and the clean male scent of his skin. He was taller than she was, easily six feet three or four, she estimated, and it was quite a novelty to meet a man who made her feel small.

But what was more unsettling was the fact that she was so aware of him. Of every little thing about him, actually, and that was definitely a new experience for her. A new experience, and one she didn't quite know how to handle. She'd never considered herself odd in any way because she was still a virgin at thirty. But suddenly the ramifications of her inexperience were beating a frantic path to her door.

But she wasn't here to learn about her own inadequacies, she chided herself. Or to observe his appearance—she drew the line at 'admire'—she added, as he crossed his arms over his midriff and regarded her with keen, assessing eyes. Green eyes, she saw, not dark as she'd first imagined, with long straight lashes that any woman would have died for.

'Your name's Claiborne?'

He repeated the question, and Rachel had to drag her eyes away from his fascinating tattoo to acknowledge his enquiry. 'Um—that's right,' she said. And then, with more daring than she'd given herself credit for, 'Does the name mean something to you?'

He seemed to hesitate. His dark brows drew together and the green of his irises deepened so that Rachel understood why she'd originally mistaken their colour. 'Perhaps,' he said at last. 'I have—heard of it. It's not a common name.'

'No, it's not.'

Rachel concentrated on not pursing her lips, but she was tempted to ask where he'd heard of it before. Would he be truthful? She doubted it. But she wondered what he'd say if she told him that Sara Claiborne was her mother.

'Anyway,' he added, apparently indifferent to her ambivalence, 'I hope you find your accommodation satisfactory.' He nodded towards the young man who was waiting patiently beside her suitcase. 'If there's anything else you need, just pick up the phone. I'm sure either the housekeeper or whoever's on Reception will be able to help you.'

'Thank you.'

The polite words almost stuck in her throat, but Rachel wasn't about to air her grievances in public. Despite the adrenalin that was still pumping through her veins, she couldn't deny she was weary.

It had been a long flight to Jamaica, and an unusually stressful final leg on the inter-island turboprop that had brought her from Montego Bay. The small plane had seemed to hit every air pocket over the Caribbean, and Rachel's legs had felt decidedly shaky when she'd stepped down onto the tarmac at St Antoine airport.

She would be glad to shed her clothes and take a long cool shower. And then maybe Room Service, if the hotel provided such a thing. She was enchanted by the island; she loved the individuality of the hotel. But Matt—Matthew—Brody's presence was a definite complication.

And it certainly didn't help her case to know that she was aware of him in a totally inappropriate way.

Now, forcing a thin smile, she left the reception desk to accompany the young man, Toby, across the foyer to the stairs. But she was fairly sure at least two pairs of eyes watched their progress, and she had to suppress the urge to swing her hips to show them that she didn't care.

Or was she being paranoid? And conceited? Matt Brody had given her no reason to believe he had found anything interesting about her. Only her name had struck a chord with him. And if what she suspected was true that was hardly surprising.

As she'd anticipated earlier, the rooms on the upper landing overlooked the foyer below. But inside they were light and airy, with a balcony opening off the outer wall that overlooked the gardens at the back of the hotel.

After assuring himself that she had everything she needed, Toby departed and Rachel took a few moments to explore her domain. The room wasn't large, but it was comfortable, with a large colonial-style bed, and a writing table and two armchairs.

There were chairs on the balcony, too, protected from the balcony next door by a trellis of flowering vines. Below, a kidney-shaped swimming pool dozed in the afternoon sun. The pool area was deserted at present, except for a couple of children who were playing tag around the striped umbrellas that provided shade from the blistering heat.

In other circumstances Rachel would have been enchanted. Objectively, the island was everything she could have hoped it would be. But, like all paradises, there had to be a serpent, and despite his fascination Matt Brody certainly fitted the bill.

Fascination?

Where the hell had that come from? Rachel was appalled at the way her mind had latched onto the word. Had she forgotten why she was here, or were her hormones playing tricks on her? For heaven's sake, this was not the time to find a man could be both dangerous and sexy.

The bathroom was functional, but efficient. Rachel took a long cooling shower and then dressed in the men's boxers and strappy vest she usually wore to bed. She was glad to shed the fine woollen pants and navy blazer she'd worn to travel from London; February in St Antoine was much different from February back home.

An examination of the hotel information assured her that she could order room service if she wanted. She wasn't particularly hungry—it was already midnight back in England, and normally she'd have been tucked up in bed by now—but if she didn't have something she'd be starving by the time it came to breakfast.

A green salad and ice-cream seemed innocuous enough, and while she waited she went out onto the balcony. It was dark outside, but the gardens were illuminated, casting shadows everywhere. The air was exotic, velvety-soft, and scented with a dozen unfamiliar fragrances. Rachel rested her hands on the rail and breathed deeply, trying to inhale the memory into her lungs.

She'd forgotten she was only wearing the boxer shorts and tight-fitting vest. As she raised her arms above her head her breasts moved freely beneath the cloth. She felt curiously free and elemental. The night air moved like a sensual finger against her skin.

And then she saw him. Well, she was almost sure that it was Matt Brody, standing in the shadow of one of the sunshades, his head turned upward towards her balcony.

She recoiled immediately, pulling down her hands and stepping back out of sight. Dear God, had he seen her? Well, of course he had. But what was he doing out there anyway? Surely he didn't live at the hotel.

A tap at her door had her panicking again. But then she remembered Room Service, and hastily pulled on a cotton wrapper over her vest and shorts. It was a young man she hadn't seen before, his eyes dark and admiring as they travelled over the curling dampness of her hair and the curving shape of her figure, barely concealed by the thin wrap.

'Enjoy your supper, Ms Claiborne,' he said, accepting the tip she offered with easy approval. And Rachel recognised how differently she'd reacted to two almost equally attractive men.

She ate all the salad and most of the ice-cream, nibbling on a sweetened wafer as she clambered between the sheets of the big bed. Her hair was still damp, and she supposed she ought to dry it. And she would, she told herself sleepily, as soon as she'd finished her biscuit.

It was light when Rachel awakened. She hadn't pulled the drapes the night before and the sun was streaming in through the balcony doors. At least she'd closed the door, she reflected, pushing back her hair with a lazy hand. Though the idea of anyone climbing over her balcony and invading her room was as far-fetched as her dreams.

It was only seven o'clock, but it was already far too warm in the room. She'd turned off the air-conditioning the night before, but now she pushed her legs out of bed and trudged across the carpeted floor to turn it on again. The rough shag tickled her toes, but the cool tiles in the bathroom provided a welcome contrast.

She examined her face in the mirror above the handbasin. Despite the troubling content of her dreams, she'd slept reasonably well. There were slight shadows around her eyes, and she was sure she'd acquired another wrinkle. But her skin was clear, albeit too fair for her liking, and although she'd never consider herself beautiful, her features were acceptable, she supposed.

She sighed, and, reaching for her toothbrush, started her morning routine. Nothing too complicated, just a cream cleanser to freshen her skin and a perfumed deodorant.

She still hadn't decided what she was going to do about speaking to Matt—Matthew Brody again. Or indeed how she was supposed to contact her mother. It would probably be too much to hope that she was staying at this hotel. Her father didn't have an address for her, but Rachel suspected she might be staying with the man she'd come to meet.

And where did he live?

She dressed in a short pleated skirt that left a tolerable length of leg bare and a daffodil-yellow tank top. She wore flip-flops instead of the heels she'd worn to travel in, acknowledging that if she did see Matt Brody he would seem that much taller and—maybe—intimidating.

But she didn't want to think about that. Leaving her room, she closed the door and, after glancing up and down the landing, she headed towards the stairs.

A middle-aged couple, just coming out of the room next door, said, 'Good morning'. Rachel returned their greeting with a smile, noticing how pale her skin looked beside theirs. Evidently they'd been here for several days. The man, who was fairer, was already exhibiting signs of sunburn.

At the other end of the landing a pair of double doors provided an effective barrier. As she went down the stairs Rachel wondered what was beyond them. Offices, perhaps, or a boardroom? Or the private apartment of the owner of the hotel?

Shrugging, she decided that could wait until later. She followed her neighbours down to the lobby, noticing that they knew their way around. For obvious reasons, she hadn't ventured out of her rooms again the night before.

The receptionist—not Rosa this time, but another girl—called a greeting, and Rachel had to admit that the staff were very friendly. Was it company policy, she wondered cynically, or were they just naturally gregarious people?

Like Matt Brody?

But she didn't want to go there, so instead she trailed her neighbours across the lobby and through open double doors into a casual dining area. Some of the tables were occupied inside, but most people who were there seemed to have opted for the patio. Leaving the others behind, Rachel stepped out into the sunshine with a feeling of optimism she couldn't suppress.

'Table for two?'

A waitress appeared at her elbow, and Rachel pulled a wry face. 'Just for one,' she said, half apologetically, and was unaccountably pleased when the young woman looked surprised.

She was seated at the far side of the patio. It was still early—barely eight o'clock—but the sun was already gaining in strength. She was glad of the awning that protected the tables. She didn't want to start her trip with sunstroke.

She drank freshly squeezed fruit juice and several cups of strong black coffee. Jamaica was famous for its coffee, and unless this was home-grown Rachel suspected she was enjoying a Jamaican blend. She ate only a warm roll and a Danish pastry, passing up French toast and maple pancakes, despite their delightfully appetising smell.

She was tempted to go for a swim after breakfast. Her usual routine, when she was on holiday, was to go sightseeing in the morning, before the sun became too unbearable, and then swim or sunbathe in the afternoon. But she wasn't on holiday, she reminded herself, as if any remainder was necessary. And as far as sightseeing was concerned, wasn't she more likely to find her quarry here?

She was lingering over one final cup of coffee when she became aware that someone had stopped beside her table. Someone who was tall and dark and disturbingly familiar, so that her nerves tingled and her breathing quickened, and she really had no need to look up from her abstract contemplation to find out who it was.

But of course she did.

'Good morning, Ms Claiborne.'

Matt Brody's voice caused the little hairs on the back of her neck to rise expectantly. Rachel found herself putting up a hand to calm them, half surprised to find the stubby ponytail she'd made of her hair that morning was still in place.

'Um—good morning.'

Her brief appraisal told her everything about him, and that was worrying. He, too, was wearing shorts this morning, cargo shorts that exposed brown legs and muscled calves. A white body shirt clung to every heft and sinew of his torso, once again revealing the arrow of air on his stomach.

Oh, God!

Rachel couldn't understand why she was so aware of him. Of all the men she'd ever met, and goodness knew there'd been plenty, why did she feel such a powerful reaction when Matt Brody was near?

Like mother, like daughter, perhaps?

But she refused to go there.

'Did you sleep well?'

Rachel decided she'd get a crick in her neck if she was forced to look up at him. Pushing back her chair, she got to her feet, but she still had to tilt her head to meet his gaze. Green eyes—were they mocking her?—looked mild and inoffensive. But why was he bothering with her? Had he guessed why she was here?

'Very well, thank you,' she answered, aware of the crispness of her tone. 'Did you?'

'I always sleep well, Ms Claiborne,' he said, his thin lips twitching with what could only be amusement. He paused. 'I wondered if you had any plans for this morning.'

Rachel's jaw nearly dropped. 'Plans?' she said somewhat blankly. And then, deciding he couldn't possibly know what she was thinking, she added, 'I—why, no. I was just considering my options, actually.'

Like, should I try and find out where you live, and whether my mother is staying in your house? Or if I should just wait and see what happens if you tell her that I'm here?

'Good.' He gave her a swift appraisal, and Rachel felt as if those shrewd green eyes had stripped her naked and found her wanting. 'So how do you feel about seeing a little more of the island?'

Once again Rachel felt that sense of disbelief that had accompanied his first question. 'I—yes,' she said, not at all sure what she was committing to, but prepared to take it anyway.

'I was thinking about that myself.' She took a breath. 'Are there guided tours?'

'You could say that.'

Matt grinned, and Rachel's stomach quivered in response. When he was relaxed, as now, he looked quite devastating, his eyes crinkling at the corners, their expression softening his masculine features.

'I was offering my services, actually,' he murmured. 'I was born in England, but apart from college I've lived all my life on St Antoine. I know this place—intimately.' Had he used that word deliberately? 'I guess I know places the guidebooks couldn't know.'

Rachel was sure he did. But she wasn't half as sure about taking him up on his invitation. It was an ideal opportunity to question him without giving herself away. But it was also far too attractive a proposition, and she wasn't at all certain her father would approve.

'Um—will anyone else be coming with us?' she asked, innocently, and for a moment she thought his eyes darkened with sudden impatience.

'No,' he said at last, his tone flat. 'Does that bother you? If I promise to keep my hands off you, will you come?'

Rachel's face flamed with colour. 'Oh, I—that is, I wasn't implying—'

'Yes, you were.' He gave a careless shrug. 'So? What's your answer?'

Rachel let out a nervous breath. 'Do I need to bring anything?' she asked, holding up her head, and his mouth twisted consideringly.

'What did you have in mind?' he queried. And then, as if aware of her embarrassment, he took pity on her. 'Just some sunscreen, I guess. And your swimsuit, if you have one.'

Rachel put a little space between them. 'All right,' she said, mentally assuring herself that her swimsuit was the last thing she'd be putting in her bag. 'When do we leave?'

He glanced at the thick gold watch on his wrist. 'Is fifteen minutes long enough?'

Rachel nodded. 'I should think so.'

His smile was ironic. 'A woman who doesn't need the better part of an hour to get ready. How lucky am I?'

We'll see, thought Rachel, but she didn't make any comment. She was already feeling apprehensive about her decision. Regretting it, no. Fearing it, yes.

'Then I'll see you in the foyer in fifteen minutes,' he said, and with a polite nod he strode into the hotel.

Rachel had to sit down for a minute after he'd left her. She told herself it was so she could finish her coffee, but the truth was her legs felt decidedly weak.

Dear God, what had she let herself in for?

But she couldn't sit here indefinitely, she thought. She needed to go back to her room and collect the sunscreen he'd mentioned. She was determined not to take a swimsuit, though she was aware that her skirt was almost as revealing. But then when she'd packed her suitcase for the trip she hadn't expected her mother's—what? Boyfriend? Lover?—would be, at the most, ten years older than herself.

Oh, to hell with it, she chided herself impatiently. She might be a virgin, but she was still capable of taking care of herself. On her father's advice, she'd taken classes in both karate and tae-kwon-do, and although she wasn't a black belt in either, her height made her a worthy opponent.

She pulled her backpack out of the wardrobe and stowed suncream and her dark glasses inside. Then, snatching up the one-piece black swimsuit she'd bought the previous year in Barcelona, she packed that, too, adding one of the hotel's towels and daring Brody to object.

A glance in the mirror above the vanity had her pulling her hair free from the scrunchie. She usually wore it straight, but she hadn't brought her tongs with her. In consequence, it spiked up at the ends, just past her shoulders. She combed her fingers through its silky strands and decided it would have to do.

It was almost exactly fifteen minutes later when she left the room. And. to her surprise, she saw Matt Brody just coming out of the double doors at the end of the landing. So did he live in the hotel, or had he just been checking up on his house guest? she wondered. If the doors were unlocked, she might check it out herself later in the day.

A shiver of anticipation glided down her spine and she hurried down the stairs ahead of him. This was proving to be more exciting than she'd thought. She pretended she hadn't seen Matt, hoping to reach the foyer before he did. But she should have known he would be wise to a move like that.

'No hurry,' he remarked, closing the gap between them. A surprisingly callused palm closed on her bare shoulder. 'I'm right behind you.'

Rachel felt the heat of that momentary possession pass through her body like an electric current. It was only momentary, because she stumbled forward in an effort to shake him off. And almost succeeded in breaking her neck when her foot came out of one of her flip-flops. She felt herself pitching forward, her arms flailing helplessly for the rail.

But then Matt's arm slipped around her waist, dragging her back from certain disaster. Well, one disaster, anyway, Rachel taunted herself silently, feeling a hysterical desire to laugh. Being hauled up against Brody's pelvis was hardly the safest thing. She was almost sure she could feel his body stirring against her, and that offered what might be greater dangers than she'd ever anticipated.

'Th-thank you.'

Somehow she managed to extricate herself from his hold, pick up the offending flip-flop and complete the staircase on one bare foot. Then, reaching the lobby, she hastily lifted her leg and restored her footwear. In the normal way she would have bent over to accomplish the task, but the idea of giving her rescuer an uninterrupted view of her bottom was not something she wanted to pursue.

Particularly not at present.

'You okay?'

Matt came round her as she was lowering her foot to the floor again, and Rachel managed a careless nod.

'As I'll ever be, I suppose,' she declared lightly. 'It's my fault for wearing these things.' She indicated the flip-flops. 'I'd have been better off in flats.'

'You'd have been better off if you hadn't tried to outrun me,' Matt replied drily. 'What's the matter, Ms Claiborne? Do I make you nervous?'

Rachel was about to deny it, but then changed her mind. 'Perhaps a little,' she admitted tightly. 'I'm not a very tactile person, I'm afraid.'

Matt arched dark brows. 'Maybe what you mean is you're only tactile with people you like.'

'I neither like nor dislike you, Mr Brody,' she retorted, realising he was going to be more difficult than she had even imagined. She glanced towards the palm-fringed forecourt. 'Do you have a car?'

Matt regarded her silently for a long moment, and she was half afraid he was going to blow her off. She didn't want that, she realised. However reckless that made her. But, after all, this was why she'd come to St Antoine.

Then, with a casual flick of his shoulders, he gestured that she should lead the way outside. And Rachel did so, supremely aware of him following her. She should have worn her Capri pants, she thought. They would have been far more suitable. She felt totally exposed in the short cotton skirt.

CHAPTER THREE

THERE were several cars on the forecourt, some of them owned by members of the hotel staff, she assumed. Few of the guests would have their own vehicle. Unless there was a hiring franchise at the airport.

She paused, waiting for Matt to point out his car, but he passed her without a word. He headed towards the gates and she saw an open-topped Jeep parked in the street outside.

So what did that mean? she wondered. Had he just arrived at the hotel this morning? Or had the Jeep been parked there all night?

Not that he was likely to tell her. He swung open the near-side door and waited until Rachel had folded herself into the front seat. If he noticed her attempt to keep her skirt from disappearing up her thighs, she was unaware of it. But then he took her backpack from her and slung it into the back of the vehicle, apparently uncaring what might break.

'Oh, I need my sunglasses,' she objected, but Matt just ignored her and walked round to get into the driving seat.

'Try these,' he said, tossing an expensive pair of designer glasses into her lap. And, although she was sure they would be far too big for her, they fitted her face like a glove.

'Thanks.'

She glanced sideways at him as he started the engine, wondering if she dared ask him who the glasses belonged to. They were evidently not his. He'd donned a pair of Raybans as soon as he'd taken his seat, their dark lenses successfully concealing his expression.

But she said nothing, forcing herself to look about her as Matt drove away from the hotel. The small town was buzzing, even this early in the morning, with local people and tourists milling about the narrow streets.

They passed close to an open-air market, and Rachel could smell fresh fish and garlic and exotic vegetables, all mingling with the musky scents of animals and humanity. A stall selling straw hats reminded Rachel that she hadn't brought any protection. It was all right as long as the Jeep was bustling through the air, but she guessed she'd feel the heat on her head if she left the car.

However, she refused to ask Matt to stop so she could buy a hat. She would have to take care she didn't spend too long in the sun. And she probably wouldn't have the chance, she mused, judging by the speed with which Matt was driving. She had the suspicion that he was now as unenthusiastic about this outing as she was.

And that was her fault. She knew it. She had behaved quite rudely back at the hotel. It wasn't his fault that she wasn't used to being handled. He'd only saved her from a nasty fall, for heaven's sake. Not mauled her for his own ends.

The streets were quieter now. They were leaving the town behind, and now children played freely in the road, apparently indifferent to passing traffic. If Rachel had expected Matt to be impatient at having to brake every couple of minutes she couldn't have been more wrong. Instead he waved at the reckless youngsters, answering their greetings, proving how well-known and obviously well-liked he was with them.

The air was getting warmer and more humid. Rachel could see the dampness on Matt's forehead and felt a trickle of perspiration running down between her breasts. What she wasn't prepared for was Matt pulling up his shirt and using it to fan his stomach, the hair around his navel glistening with sweat.

Rachel's own stomach quivered in protest. Dear God, he was such a physical man. She discovered that, contrary to previous experiences, she wasn't immune to this man's sexuality. Quite the reverse, in fact. She wanted to reach out and touch him, to brush her fingers over that provocative growth of hair and feel the smoothness of taut brown skin.

The knowledge horrified her. As far as she knew this was the man her mother had flown over three thousand miles to see. Whatever their relationship—and she couldn't believe, having met him, that it was just friendship—her father certainly didn't expect her to get involved with him herself.

Having left the final cottages behind, they were now driving towards the ocean. Behind them, the mountains she'd seen from the taxi crowded closely towards the road. Thick vegetation turned their slopes into a lush green carpet, but ahead rough acres of uncultivated grasses descended inevitably towards the sea.

Rachel, who had been trying to remain detached about her feelings, couldn't deny a breath of wonder at the sight of blue-green water lapping a beach of pure white sand.

'It's so beautiful,' she said in a hushed voice, barely aware that they were the first words she'd spoken since they left the hotel.

Matt cast a fleeting glance in her direction, before agreeing that this was a pretty part of the island. 'Mango Cove,' he said after a moment. 'St Antoine is reputedly one of a series of peaks from an underwater mountain range. Jamaica is another.'

'Really?'

Rachel was fascinated, and Matt went on to explain that the Spaniards had first settled here at the beginning of the sixteenth century. 'Then, when Jamaica became a British colony, they ignored this island and it was later taken over by the French. San Antonio became St Antoine. End of story.'

Rachel shook her head. 'I can't understand anyone not wanting to hold on to such a beautiful place,' she protested.

'Economics, I suppose.' They'd reached a bluff above the sand dunes and Matt brought the Jeep to a halt overlooking the bay. 'Jamaica offered so much, whereas this place must have appeared to offer so little.' He pulled a wry face. 'Hey, I'm grateful. At least St Antoine isn't overrun with beach resorts and hotels.'

Rachel half turned in her seat to look at him. 'The taxi driver told me that—that the Brodys own most of the island. That would be you, right?'

Matt pulled off his dark glasses to look at her through narrowed eyes. 'Now, why would a taxi driver tell you something like that?' he asked, and for a moment Rachel didn't have an answer.

She was certainly not prepared to confront him about her mother at the moment. When—or even if—she did so, she would hope it was in a place less isolated than this. But at the same time she had to say something. Even if he must suspect her motives just as much as she suspected his.

'I—er—I was asking him about the plots of land around the houses. I said I thought they were cute, but he said the tenants didn't own them. That—that the Brodys did.'

'Really?' Matt looked sceptical. 'Well, for your information, the island people *do* own their own plots of land.' He gave her one final speculative glance and then thrust open his door. 'We encourage people to be self-sufficient.' His lips twisted. 'Your taxi driver got it wrong.'

'So it would seem.' Rachel kept a wary eye on him as he got out of the Jeep. Then, pushing open her own door, she did likewise, feeling the heat of the sun on her arms and the delicious breeze off the water.

Matt pushed his glasses back onto his nose and went ahead

of her. Slipping and sliding, he descended the dunes to arrive unscathed at the beach.

He turned then. 'You coming?' he asked, and Rachel decided she didn't have much choice. Besides, she wanted to paddle in the water. Her feet were already itching to feel the sand between her toes.

Hauling her backpack out of the back of the Jeep, she removed the flip-flops and then followed him. It wasn't as easy going down the dunes as he'd made it look, and she arrived at the bottom dishevelled and red-faced.

Thankfully, Matt had already walked away towards the water. And, putting down her pack, she combed her fingers through her hair again, realising that trying to look neat at the moment was far beyond her capabilities.

Shouldering the pack again, she started after him, and then paused for a second to examine a huge pink shell that was honeycombed with cracks. Evidently something had lived inside it once, but its sanctuary had been invaded. Or perhaps it was very old and had been eroded by the sea.

The sun was beginning to beat down on her head now, as well as on her shoulders. When she straightened, she lifted a hand to protect her scalp.

'You hot now?'

Her interest in the shell had not gone unnoticed, and Matt had made his way back to her. Like her, he'd shed the Converse trainers he'd been wearing, tying the laces together and hanging them round his neck.

'A bit,' Rachel admitted, and Matt nodded towards the sea.

'Take a dip,' he advised. 'That will cool you down. You might even enjoy it.'

Rachel pursed her lips. 'How do you know I've brought a swimsuit?'

Matt pulled off his glasses again, his eyes mocking and

intent. 'Hey, I'm not a prude,' he said. 'We can go skinny-dipping, if you like. I'm game if you are.'

Why did he always have the power to embarrass her? As her face flamed with colour, Rachel hoped it would just blend in with the flush that already stained her cheeks.

'I know you're not serious,' she said primly, although she was half afraid he was. 'But I have brought a swimsuit, as it happens. If you'll look the other way, I'll put it on.'

Matt's mouth showed his amusement. 'Now who's a prude?' he asked. 'I can't believe you've never undressed in front of a man before.'

As a matter of fact she hadn't, but Rachel wasn't about to tell him that. 'Just turn the other way,' she said tersely. 'I'm not about to undress in front of a man I barely know.'

'Your loss.'

But to her relief he did turn his back and saunter away towards the ocean. Though her deliverance was tempered with disbelief when he hauled his shirt over his head and flung it down on the sand. Then his hands went to the waistband of his shorts.

Rachel's mouth fell open and she paused in the middle of unbuttoning her skirt. What on earth was he doing? she wondered. And then let out a gasp when he dropped his shorts as well.

He was wearing underwear.

Rachel relaxed a little when she saw black shorts. She'd been half afraid he went commando. But, dear God, what would her mother think? she mused, dumbfounded. Did she know he flirted with other women when she wasn't around?

And yet he hadn't actually flirted with her, she conceded honestly, stripping off her skirt and panties, pulling her swimsuit over her hips. It wasn't his fault that she reacted to him. He was just naturally unconventional, naturally uninhibited, the kind of man Rachel had never had dealings with before.

Her tank top and bra were quickly disposed of, and she

expelled another sigh when the top of the swimsuit was securely in place. Okay, it was strapless, and probably not the
most appropriate choice in these circumstances. But she'd
change back into her clothes as soon as she'd had a swim.

Matt was already in the water, the sea lapping about his
hips. His tattoo was fully exposed now, wrapped darkly
around his upper arm. She noticed how brown his skin was
above his black waistband, smooth and unblemished. He had
narrow hips and strong thighs and a tight muscled butt.

Dear Lord, she wasn't supposed to notice such things, not
about a man who was apparently involved with her mother.
But, for some reason she preferred not to dwell on, she was
incapable of ignoring him, or his hard masculine beauty.

Choosing a spot some yards from where Matt had entered
the water, Rachel dragged her eyes away from her tormentor
and ran eagerly into the sea. It was so good to submerge her
shoulders, to dip her head below the surface, to come up feeling exhilarated just to be alive.

The land shelved fairly steeply, she discovered, and in no
time at all she was out of her depth. But that didn't worry her.
She was a strong swimmer, and the water itself was so warm
and soft and delightful. Whatever else she took from this trip,
she would always remember swimming in the Caribbean.

She'd been half afraid that as soon as she was in the water
Matt would join her. Or was that half hopeful? she wondered,
aware of something like disappointment when he kept away.
He was some distance further out, turned onto his back and
floating on the water. A dark star-shaped figure that attracted
her like a magnet.

She couldn't help herself. She swam towards him and said
breathlessly, 'Isn't it marvellous? I've never swum in water
as clear as this.' She'd already noticed dozens of tiny fish
swimming beneath her. 'Thank you for bringing me here.'

'No problem.'

With knife-like grace, Matt brought his legs up to his body

and then straightened to tread water beside her. He'd left his dark glasses on the beach, as she had, and his eyes were unmistakably sardonic.

'I got the impression you wished you hadn't accepted my invitation,' he said, reaching out to wipe a strand of wet hair from her face. He saw her flinch and his expression hardened. 'Lighten up, can't you? Or do you think every man who touches you wants to jump your bones?'

'I'm sure you don't, Mr Brody,' she retorted, her enjoyment of the day souring on the bitterness of his words. Without waiting for his response, she turned and swam back towards the shore. He was impossible, she thought irritably. He turned everything into a personal assault.

Matt overtook her before she reached the shallows, so she was obliged to follow him as he walked up out of the water. But she found her stomach tightening instinctively when she got a good look at his underwear. He was wearing black stretch boxers that clung to him like a second skin.

He turned, picking up his body shirt and using it to dry his chest and stomach. As before, he didn't seem to care what she thought of his behaviour, but Rachel was finding it very hard to drag her eyes away. It infuriated her, but she found everything about him unbearably sexy. She was beginning to understand why the girls in the office gossiped constantly about their sexual experiences.

The bravado of bringing one of the hotel towels seemed unnecessary now. Rachel felt distinctly guilty when she pulled the towel out of her backpack. But Matt wasn't looking at her. As he continued to rub his chest and arms, his attention seemed fixed on a large bird foraging among debris further along the sand.

Rachel couldn't help herself. Wrapping the towel about her, she exclaimed, 'What is that?'

'A pelican.' Matt sounded indifferent. 'It's evidently found something to eat amongst the seaweed. This beach is usually deserted. I guess it thought it wouldn't be disturbed.'

'A pelican.' Rachel shook her head in wonder. 'I've never seen a pelican before.' She looked at Matt. 'Is that what you've got tattooed on your arm?'

'Hell, no.' Matt shook his head, though his gaze barely acknowledged her. 'This is a nighthawk. I had it done while I was at college. My father didn't approve, but it was too late then to do anything about it.' He grimaced. 'Finish getting dressed. Then I'll take you back to the hotel.'

'Oh.' Rachel let out a sigh. 'Must we?'

Matt's frown wasn't encouraging. 'Must we what?'

'Go back,' Rachel said, knowing he'd understood her the first time. 'Look, I know I overreacted before, but that's just me.'

'Really?'

His frown deepened, but he didn't immediately say anything else. Instead, to her amazement, he turned his back on her and pushed his wet boxers down his legs.

Rachel's eyes widened. She'd been right. He was totally uninhibited. He didn't care who saw him, or that she might find his behaviour offensive.

But she couldn't deny he was good to look at. Wide shoulders tapered to narrow hips, his buttocks rounded and tight. And he was brown all over. No boring privacy line for him. As he used his shirt to dry himself again, Rachel found she was holding her breath.

She didn't suck another gulp of air into her labouring lungs until he'd pulled on his cargo shorts. He wrung out the boxers he'd worn to swim in, and then put on the damp body shirt that clung even closer now. She could count the vertebrae in his spine, the neat lacing of muscles over his stomach. And then she realised, with a sense of frustration, that she hadn't even begun to get dressed herself.

Fool, she thought impatiently. She was acting like a moon-

struck schoolgirl. Heaven knew what her mother would think
if she could see her now.

She fumbled beneath the towel, trying to dislodge the
swimsuit. But her body was wet, the suit damp and clingy.
She couldn't help thinking how much easier it would be if she
dared drop the towel and strip in front of him.

Of course she didn't do any such thing. And to her relief
Matt bent to gather up his shoes. With a supreme effort she
managed to kick the swimsuit off her legs. It was fairly simple,
after that, to step into her skirt and panties using the towel to
protect her as she pulled on her tank top.

It was only as she was stuffing the damp towel into her
backpack that she saw her bra still lying on the sand. She said
a rude word under her breath, but it was too late to worry
about it now. She stuffed it into the bag, too, suddenly aware
that Matt had started away along the shoreline.

He glanced back when she straightened, however, and his
timing was so perfect she had to wonder if he'd been as indifferent to her struggles as she'd believed.

'Let's walk,' he said neutrally, apparently prepared to
humour her. 'If you can stand the heat.'

'I think I can.'

Rachel slung the backpack over her shoulder and hurried
to catch up with him. But when she came level he reached
over and lifted the bag from her arm.

'Leave it here,' he said, dropping it onto the sand. He spread
an all-encompassing arm. 'No one's likely to steal it.' He
pulled a wry face. 'Except him, of course.' He indicated the
pelican, who looked poised for flight. 'But I doubt he'd find
one of my towels to his taste.'

Rachel glanced up at him. 'I know. I shouldn't have brought
it.'

'Did I say that?'

'You didn't have to. I feel guilty enough as it is.'

'Forget it.' He dismissed her claim. 'What's one towel or more between enemies?'

Rachel caught her breath. 'Are we enemies, Mr Brody?'

'Matt,' he corrected her shortly. And then, 'Well, we're sure as hell not friends.' He started to walk again. 'Come on. Keep moving. Or you're going to need to cover up.'

Which wasn't his problem, thought Rachel, trying to distract herself. But if she wanted to stay with him she had to do as he said. And it was surprisingly pleasant, walking in the shallows, feeling the sand melting away between her toes.

They walked for a while in silence. Rachel had expected to feel uncomfortable after what he'd just said, but she didn't. In actual fact she enjoyed the sense of isolation, with only the cry of birds and the muted thunder of the ocean to disturb the peace.

And then he asked the question she'd been dreading.

'Why did you come to St Antoine, Ms Claiborne?'

CHAPTER FOUR

MATT had halted and Rachel was forced to do the same.

She took a breath. 'My name's Rachel, as I'm sure you know.'

'Okay.' He was tolerant. 'Why did you come to St Antoine, *Rachel*?'

She couldn't tell him. Not like this. Not so baldly. She just couldn't.

'Um—why do people usually come to the island?' she prevaricated lightly. 'I needed a break and St Antoine seemed an ideal place to chill.'

'To chill?'

Sceptical eyes drifted down over the defensive angle of her jaw to the creamy hollow of her throat.

And beyond.

Rachel was instantly aware of the disadvantages of not wearing a bra when his eyes lingered on her cleavage. The hard peaks of her breasts must be clearly visible, taut against the soft fabric of her top. And, short of covering them with her hands, there was nothing she could do about it.

'You should have gone to the South Pole,' he remarked mockingly. 'I'm told it's pretty chilly there.'

Rachel's nostrils flared. 'I think you know what I meant.'

'Yeah.'

He conceded the point and started walking again. And

Rachel was so relieved to be free of those scathing eyes she fell into step beside him.

But he wasn't finished.

'That doesn't really explain why you chose this island,' he persisted. 'I mean, we're not exactly on the tourist map.'

'You get tourists here.'

'They're often recommendations,' Matt informed her smoothly. 'And usually from the States.'

Rachel managed a short laugh. 'You know, if I didn't know better, I'd think that you didn't welcome new visitors, Mr Brody. If all your guests are subjected to this inquisition.'

'Matt.' He stopped again, his voice hardening with impatience. 'And they're not.'

'Oh.' Rachel made a moue of her lips. 'Well, I'm here now.' She paused. 'I'm sorry if I'm in the way.'

Matt studied her apparently innocent expression for another long disturbing moment, and then made a chopping movement with his hand.

'Did I say you were in the way?' he demanded. 'You—intrigue me, that's all. Put it down to simple curiosity, if you like, but I don't think you're being entirely honest about your reasons for being here.'

What did he know?

Rachel sucked in a breath. 'Are you calling me a liar, Mr Brody?'

'Don't put words in my mouth, Ms Claiborne. There's an expression I've heard that seems relevant. I think you're being economical with the truth.'

Rachel turned away and started walking again. She could feel his eyes boring into the back of her head, but she forced herself to put one foot in front of the other.

'I must say, you don't pull your punches, Mr Brody,' she threw back over her shoulder. 'And here was I, thinking you'd enjoyed my company.'

'Whether or not I enjoy your company has nothing to do

with it,' he retorted, overtaking her. He stepped in front of her. 'And for God's sake stop calling me *Mr* Brody.'

Rachel made an effort to appear composed. But it was difficult with approximately two hundred pounds of frustrated male more or less in her face.

'All right. *Matt*,' she said with assumed lightness. 'You don't have to humour me. I'm not what you expected and I suspect you don't like me very much.'

He blew out a breath. 'Now, where the hell did that come from?' His eyes darkened. 'But you're right. You're not what I expected.'

Rachel felt a twinge of disappointment. But why should he be any different from other men? And, more importantly, why did it matter? He was her mother's problem, not hers.

'I think we should go back,' she said, concentrating on the unbuttoned neckline of his body shirt. Which wasn't the most sensible place to look, bearing in mind the dark hair that was clearly visible in the opening. But at least it kept her gaze away from his. 'It's been very—enjoyable, but all good things must—'

'You know, that's part of the problem,' he said, ignoring her suggestion completely. His voice had thickened to a sensual drawl. 'You're not like any woman I've known before.'

'And I'm sure you've known many,' Rachel retorted before she could stop herself. But, heavens, what was she supposed to say?

'Some,' he agreed, his eyes darkening with a predatory gleam, and Rachel couldn't help herself. She started backing away. But he came after her. 'Does that bother you, Ms Claiborne? The fact that I don't want to like you but I do?'

Rachel's jaw dropped. 'Are you coming on to me, Mr— *Matt*? Because I think I should warn you, I do know how to defend myself.'

'Oh, for heaven's sake!' With a muffled oath, Matt strode past her. 'Listen to yourself, will you?' His long legs opened a yawning space between them. 'Get your rucksack. We're going back.'

'It's a backpack,' muttered Rachel barely audibly as she hurried after him.

They'd walked a surprisingly long way, and she had to jog back to where her bag was lying before practically running to reach the place where they'd left the Jeep.

She was still muttering to herself as she struggled to climb the dunes, getting frustrated when the sand persisted in sliding away beneath her feet. She'd watched Matt navigate them without any apparent effort, and it was infuriating to see him standing at the top, watching her make an absolute idiot of herself.

'You might have helped me,' she panted when she got to the top, but Matt only lifted both hands, palms towards her.

'What? And be accused of taking advantage of one of my guests?' he mocked. 'And besides, why should I deprive myself of such an amusing exhibition?'

Rachel's lips pursed. 'Moron!'

Matt shrugged. 'Bimbo!'

Rachel gasped. 'I'm not a bimbo!'

'And I'm not a moron, Ms Claiborne. I suggest you get in the vehicle and I'll take you back to the hotel.'

Rachel wrenched open the door of the Jeep and did as he suggested. For his part, Matt pulled what she saw were the damp pair of boxers out of his pocket and tossed them into the back of the car. Then he climbed in beside her, the waistband of his shorts dipping revealingly at the back, reminding her, if any reminder was necessary, that he was naked under them.

They seemed to get back to the hotel far more quickly than Rachel had expected. In no time at all, Matt was drawing up outside the Tamarisk's gates.

Rachel thrust open her door and jumped out, turning to make some perfunctory offer of thanks. But Matt just said,

'Enjoy your day,' and drove away without giving her time to speak.

Rachel's mouth compressed frustratedly, but there was nothing she could do. He'd gone, and with him any chance of asking him about her mother. Although whether she'd have actually had the nerve to do that was anyone's guess.

Reaching her room, she found the message light on her phone was flashing. Lifting the receiver, she connected with Reception and then said, 'I believe you have a message for me.'

As she waited for the girl to reply, it crossed her mind that it could be her mother. If Matt had mentioned her arrival to her, she might have decided to get in touch.

'Ms Claiborne?'

The girl was speaking again, and Rachel answered in the positive. 'I'm here.'

'I have here a note that says your father called at nine o'clock this morning,' the receptionist intoned leisurely. 'He asked if you'd ring him as soon as you came in.'

Of course. It had to be her father, thought Rachel grumpily. He'd probably expected her to phone him last night, although bearing in mind the time change that had surely not been on the cards.

'Okay. Thank you,' she said now, and put down the receiver. She needed a few moments to compose what she was going to say before she made the call.

Eventually, though, she dialled for an outside line and punched in the numbers of her parents' home. For years they'd all lived in a comfortable house in Chingford, but when Rachel had moved into an apartment of her own her parents had sold the house and bought an apartment themselves.

'Hello?'

Her father's voice was surprisingly welcome. Despite the argument they'd had about her coming here, he was still her best friend in the entire world. She loved her mother. There was no doubt about that. But the aloofness she'd always detected in her mother's attitude towards her had made any real closeness between them difficult.

'Hey, Dad.' Rachel tried to sound upbeat. 'Sorry I was out when you called.'

'Where were you?'

Instead of making some reassuring comment, Ralph Claiborne was immediately on the offensive.

'I—I took a tour of the island,' Rachel finally replied, a little defensively. 'I was going to ring you as soon as I got back.'

'Hmmph!' Her father didn't sound mollified. 'So, what's happening? Have you spoken to your mother yet?'

'Are you kidding?' Rachel was indignant. 'We're not talking Camberwick Green here, Dad. This may be a fairly small island, but I should think its population runs into tens of thousands.'

'Does it?'

'Yes.' Rachel sighed. 'You're going to have to give me some leeway, Dad. I can't be making a report to you every single day.'

'No one's asking you to phone every single day,' he shot back, evidently on edge. 'Just keep me in the loop, Rachel. That's all I ask.'

'And I will. When I have something pertinent to tell you.' Rachel crossed her fingers, aware that she wasn't being honest with him either. 'Anyway, how are you? How are you managing on your own?'

'Oh, I'm all right.' He was dismissive. 'Your aunt Laura brought me a cooked meal last night.' He snorted. 'The damn woman can't keep away.'

'Well, you watch what you're doing,' said Rachel reprovingly. 'You know Aunt Laura's always had a soft spot for you. I'd hate you to get involved with her when Mum's probably going to be home in a couple of days.'

'You think?'

He didn't sound optimistic, and, knowing all the facts, Rachel couldn't blame him. If her mother was involved with Matt Brody, she was unlikely to want to give him up any time soon.

'Leave it to me,' she said firmly, with more confidence than circumstances allowed. 'I'll give you a ring in a couple of days, unless you hear something before I do.'

'As if I'm going to.' Her father sounded depressed now. 'Thank God I didn't retire last year as your mother wanted.'

Ralph Claiborne was an accountant, working for a small firm in Charing Cross. But now Rachel had to wonder if his refusal to retire might have been the trigger that had set the present events in motion. Maybe her mother was lonely. Still, that wasn't really an excuse for what she'd done.

'Okay, Dad,' Rachel said now. 'I'm going to go and take a shower and then have some lunch. This is a super hotel.' Owned by the Brodys. But that was something she couldn't discuss right now. 'I'm glad you chose it.'

'Well, I'm glad I've done something right, then,' said her father shortly. 'But you're not there to enjoy an unscheduled holiday, Rachel. You know what I expect you to do. Find your mother.'

'Yes, Dad.'

Rachel winced at the pain in his voice, and long after she'd replaced the receiver she sat there just staring at the phone. But without Matt Brody's help she hadn't the first idea of how she was going to find Sara Claiborne. This was the only hotel on the island, according to the taxi driver, and surely the receptionist would have made the connection if her mother was staying here.

During the next couple of days Rachel made a concerted effort to find out everything she could about alternative accommodation on the island. She found an information booth in town, and was able to get the names of several B and Bs from them. She checked them out without any luck, but she wasn't totally surprised. And there was no way she could mention her search to the receptionist at the Tamarisk without arousing more questions than answers.

On the third day she made her way down to the harbour. Despite her investigations, for the first two days she'd suffered from jet-lag and had needed to rest in the afternoons. She had gone down to the pool for a swim in the early evening, however—the water was deliciously warm then, and mostly deserted—before returning to her room to dress for dinner.

She was falling into quite a routine, and she knew she had to put a stop to it. It was far too easy to relax here, even if the sight of Matt Brody still caused goosebumps to feather her spine. She'd seen him once or twice, going in and out of the hotel, but there'd never been a confrontation. Whether that was his fault or hers, she couldn't be certain. But she was fairly sure he was avoiding her.

Which wasn't helping her father's cause at all. She knew he'd feel so betrayed if he learned she'd spoken to Matt Brody without even mentioning her mother's name.

But how could she? Rachel asked herself. She'd only spent a couple of hours in Matt's company, when all was said and done. They weren't even friends. They were more like enemies now. How could she have asked him such a personal question? *Are you having an affair with my mother?*

The harbour was as pretty as the rest of the island. Several fishing boats were anchored on one side of a small stone pier, with a surprisingly busy marina occupying the other. A number of yachts with reefed sails bobbed in the current, their distinctive mooring bells carrying musically on the breeze.

There were motor yachts, too. Huge expensive things, with tiered decks and gleaming brass furniture. One of them even had a small pool, but it was empty at present. Its owner was probably enjoying the freedom of moving from place to place.

Rachel leaned on the rail overlooking the marina. She was wearing shorts this morning, and a blue silk vest she'd bought in the hotel shop. She was admiring her slight tan when she saw a big man emerge from one of the slips. He was formally attired, in pleated khakis and a dress shirt, open at the neck. He was wearing a tie, too, pulled away from his collar. His dark hair was ruffled by the breeze, but there was no mistaking that it was Matt Brody, real and in the flesh.

Her instincts were telling her to walk away, now, before he looked up and saw her. All right, she wasn't doing anything wrong, but would he believe her being here was purely a coincidence? She remembered he'd avoided her at the hotel. Or at least made no effort to speak to her again. And after her behaviour at the beach she couldn't exactly blame him.

She guessed he'd come from one of the motor vessels. The yacht behind him wasn't the biggest in the marina, but it wasn't the smallest either. He wasn't dressed for sailing, so what was he doing here?

Despite her misgivings, she knew she ought to make an effort and speak to him. For her father's sake, if nothing else. How was she ever going to find out where her mother was if she didn't open the lines of communication, as they said in the best spy dramas? Where was the harm? If he blew her off, she could at least say she'd tried.

Rachel took a breath, preparing to call a greeting, when she saw a young woman emerge from the yacht behind him. The sound she'd been about to make was stifled in her throat. Evidently they were together. The girl was hurrying, trying to catch him up.

'Wait,' she called, her voice showing her agitation. 'Matt, wait for me. D'you want me to break my heel on these damn boards?'

She was a beautiful young woman, Rachel noticed. Not

particularly tall, but slender and graceful, with short black hair and elfin features. But right now her mouth was drawn down in a scowl, her ill humour evidently directed towards her companion.

'I didn't ask you to come here,' Matt called back over his shoulder, his voice carrying clearly over the water. And Rachel felt like a voyeur, no matter how innocent her eavesdropping might be.

'I know that,' the girl huffed as she caught up with him. She grabbed his arm familiarly and he didn't shake her off. 'But I wanted to speak to you privately and you're never around.'

Matt helped her negotiate the gate that led out of the mooring area. 'What you mean is, you don't usually get up before midday.'

'I need my sleep,' she protested, as they disappeared under the overhang of the jetty.

And Rachel realised they were probably heading for the stone stairs that she could see just a few yards away along the pier.

Once again, the urge to escape before they saw her was compelling. Whoever the girl was, Matt was evidently familiar with her sleeping habits. Which begged the question, how many women was he involved with?

However, before she could decide what she wanted to do, Matt appeared at the top of the steps. He stretched out a hand to help the young woman up beside him, and then they both started walking towards the quay. Towards Rachel.

Matt recognised her at once. Rachel thought he cast a brief glance down at his companion, but he didn't slow his stride. Whoever she was, he wasn't concerned that Rachel had seen her with him, and as before it was left to the girl to keep up with him.

'Hi.' As soon as they were within speaking distance, Rachel spoke. She was conscious that her greeting had caught the other girl unawares. 'It's a lovely morning, isn't it?'

'They're all lovely mornings on St Antoine,' replied Matt tersely, and she was sure his intention had been to walk right by her.

But the girl caught his arm again, and he came to an evidently reluctant halt. 'Except in the hurricane season,' she said, narrowing her eyes at Rachel and assessing her appearance with an intensity that was far from objective. 'Are you staying on the island? Ms—er—?'

'Rachel,' Rachel supplied a little stiffly. She knew Matt was looking at her with unconcealed impatience. Clearly he hadn't wanted to do more than acknowledge her, and then only because she'd spoken first. 'I'm staying at the Tamarisk.'

'Oh. You're staying at the hotel.' The girl raised dark brows and glanced up at the man beside her. 'How interesting.' She paused. 'Isn't it, Matt?'

Matt's response was merely to shrug his shoulders, and the girl absorbed this before turning back to Rachel to ask enquiringly. 'Are you staying long?'

Rachel objected to these questions. Particularly from someone she hadn't even been introduced to. But if she wanted to retain Matt's attention she had to be polite.

'Uh—no,' she said now. 'Just a couple of weeks, actually. I don't think the hurricane season will bother me.'

'Or Amalie either.' As if he felt compelled to make some contribution to the conversation, Matt released himself from the girl's fingers and gave Rachel an appraising look. She was instantly conscious of the limitations of narrow-legged shorts and trainers, but Matt's eyes were coolly uninterested. 'When the hurricane season comes around my sister's usually tucked up safely in New York.'

She was his sister!

Rachel's tongue ran nervously over her upper lip. It shouldn't have been such a relief to her, but it was. 'So,' she ventured, 'have you been sailing?'

'In this outfit?'

Amalie rolled her eyes, and Rachel felt foolish for having suggested such a thing.

'I was just checking out the boat,' Matt put in, apparently taking pity on her. 'We've got a group of fishermen coming in tomorrow, and they plan on taking it up to Grand Cayman.'

'Oh...' Rachel nodded. 'It's a charter.'

'Yeah, a charter.' Amalie chimed in again. 'My brother insists on checking the boats out himself.'

Rachel's eyes widened. 'You've got more than one?'

'Heavens, yes. We've got—'

'—more than one,' Matt broke in before Amalie could finish. 'And now, if you'll excuse us...'

'Actually...' Rachel wasn't accustomed to soliciting a man's company, but she had to try. 'I was wondering if you—and your sister, of course—might like to join me for a—a coffee or something.'

The girl was the first to speak. She gave Rachel a measuring look and then gazed up at Matt, her expression frankly mocking. 'Hey, I think you're being propositioned, darling,' she said musingly. 'Methinks the lady wants to get in your pants!'

CHAPTER FIVE

'FOR God's sake, Amalie!'

Matt swore, evidently infuriated by her comment, but Rachel was sure he couldn't possibly feel as bad as she did at that moment. Without knowing anything about their history— or at least Rachel didn't think she did—Amalie had assumed she was coming on to her brother.

'What? *What?*'

Amalie feigned innocence, but Rachel was sure she'd known exactly how her brother would react.

'Grow up!' said Matt harshly. 'Not all women think about sex every minute of the day. Don't judge everyone by your standards, Amalie. Keep your sordid comments to yourself.'

'All right, all right.' Amalie looked sulky now, and she lifted her hands defensively. Then she turned to Rachel. 'You weren't offended, were you?'

Rachel mumbled something non-committal, but that didn't stop Amalie from continuing. 'I mean, we're both women of the world, aren't we? And, as you're probably a little older than me, yeah, I bet you've—known quite a few exciting men in your time.'

The pause before the word 'known' wasn't lost on Rachel. She wondered what Amalie would say if she told her she was still a virgin. She probably wouldn't believe her. Most people didn't. Particularly men.

'Whether or not Rachel was offended, I was,' stated Matt

harshly. 'Take the Jeep and go back to the house, Amalie. I'll get Caleb to come and get me when I'm through.'

'Oh, but Rachel asked me to join you for a cup of coffee,' Amalie objected.

'Rachel didn't know you had to leave.' Matt's tone was unyielding. 'D'you want to argue with me?'

'No,' Amalie said broodingly. 'You know, you're no fun. I would have liked a cup of coffee, as it goes.'

'Get one back at the house,' Matt advised her tersely. And, looking at his expression, Rachel didn't think she would have argued with him either.

'But we never got to talk.' Amalie gazed up at him appealingly.

'Okay.' Matt didn't sound particularly amenable. 'How about if I promise we'll talk tonight?'

'Tonight?' Amalie wailed.

'Yeah. Be at home for dinner. We'll have plenty of time to discuss your financial problems then.'

Amalie pursed her lips. 'But what about Tony?'

'Tony Scabo?'

'Yes. I said I'd see him tonight.'

'Well, bring him to dinner. I'm sure he'll be interested to hear what you have to say.'

'Beast!' Amalie pouted. Then her eyes flickered Rachel's way. 'Just don't think I'm a fool,' she snapped shortly, and with another loaded glance in Rachel's direction she teetered away on her ridiculous heels.

'I'm sorry if I caused a problem,' Rachel murmured when his sister was out of earshot.

'Are you?' Matt didn't sound as if he believed her. 'Isn't that your role here, causing me problems?'

'I don't know what you mean.'

'No? So why are you suddenly being so friendly? The last time we were together you told me I was a moron.'

Rachel's face flamed. 'You called me a bimbo!'

'Only in self-defence.'

'Well, anyway, I was wrong. You're not a moron. I'm sorry if I was rude. Now, can we just bury our differences and move on?'

'Why?'

'Why?' She was taken aback by the question.

'Yeah. Why should you care what I think?'

'Well…' Rachel's tongue circled her lower lip this time. 'Let's just say I do.' She paused. 'Will you have coffee with me?'

'Are you coming on to me, Ms Claiborne?'

'Oh, for heaven's sake!' Rachel knew he was just being sarcastic, but that didn't alter her frustration. 'You really are the most infuriating man I've ever known.'

'And you've known quite a few—is that what you're saying? Amalie seemed to think you knew your way around.'

'Amalie was wrong,' said Rachel crossly. 'Don't let my appearance fool you, Mr Brody.'

'You mean because you have the kind of face and figure that might make a man think of sex?'

'No.' Rachel knew he was only baiting her, but she had to make some defence. 'I just wanted you to know that I don't spend my time jumping in and out of other people's beds.'

'I assume you mean *men's* beds,' Matt murmured, a hint of laughter in his voice, and she sighed.

'Can we just leave it?' she demanded. 'Do you want to join me for coffee or not?'

'Do I still have a choice?'

'Of course.'

Matt shrugged. 'Why not? If you'll promise to stop calling me *Mr* Brody.' They began to stroll back towards the quay. 'So—are you enjoying your holiday? You're not finding it lonely, being on your own?'

'Is that why you think I've asked you to have coffee with me?' she countered immediately, and Matt gave her a resigned look.

'Uh, no,' he said mildly. 'Believe it or not, it was a perfectly innocent question. But if you don't want to answer it, hey, that's all right with me.'

Rachel pressed her lips together. Somehow he always managed to make her feel small. 'As a matter of fact, I haven't had time to feel lonely. I've been exploring the town, getting over jet-lag.' She grimaced. 'It was only when I saw you that I thought I ought to take the chance to make amends for the way I behaved that first day.'

Matt cast a sideways glance at her. 'You weren't curious about Amalie's identity?'

Rachel looked away so he wouldn't see the sudden blush that filled her cheeks. 'Why should I be?' she asked. Then, 'Will you decide where we should go for coffee? Is there somewhere special that only the locals know?'

Matt said nothing for a moment, and then he gestured across the harbour road to a small café set up off the street. Rachel might never have noticed it if he hadn't pointed it out. It looked more like a night spot with its outdoor bar and seating area.

'Juno's,' he said. 'She's a good friend of mine. And she just happens to serve the best coffee in St Antoine.'

'Okay.'

Rachel was grateful for the need to dodge the traffic to give her time to compose herself again. Walking quickly, she managed to keep up with his long strides, and they crossed the sidewalk and climbed the steps to the first-floor bar. They stepped inside into an atmosphere redolent with the mingled smells of beer and tobacco and rich spicy food. And the delicious scent of dark coffee beans, roasted and strong.

Juno herself came to greet them. She was a statuesque West Indian woman, easily sixty years old, Rachel estimated, with a long angular body and incongruously dyed purple hair. She was wearing an ankle-length caftan in a multitude of colours, and a curly-headed little girl was propped on one hip.

'Hey, Brody!' she exclaimed when she saw him, and despite her burden she opened one arm and gave him a bone-crushing hug. The child protested loudly, but when Matt bent to speak to her, her lips twitched into a smile before she pushed one thumb into her mouth.

'Hey, Juno.' Matt returned her greeting. 'And this must be Patrice.'

'I'm Megan,' averred the little girl indignantly, and Juno gave her a reassuring cuddle.

'Of course.' Matt grinned at the child, and Rachel felt her stomach lurch at his blatant charm. 'Megan,' he added. 'You're getting so big I didn't recognise you.'

'Smooth-tongued devil,' said Juno in pretend disgust. 'You beware of men like this, Megan. He's all good-looks and no substance.'

Matt laughed. 'You're only jealous, old lady,' he said lightly. 'And you a woman looking half your age.'

'Oh, listen to the man!' Juno turned to Rachel, shaking her head. 'Don't you just love his prattle? But who are you, girl?' She glanced back at Matt. 'I don't think I've seen her before.'

'You haven't.' Matt lifted his shoulders, and Rachel's eyes were drawn to the strong brown column of his throat. 'This is Rachel.' His eyes met hers. 'She's staying at the hotel.'

'You don't say?' Juno studied Rachel's suddenly flushed face with interest. 'Well, she's certainly younger than the one you brought in last week.'

Rachel's jaw dropped then, and she stared at Matt wide-eyed, but his expression didn't change. If the woman's words had disconcerted him, he certainly didn't show it.

'You could be right,' he said non-committally. 'I can always rely on you to keep me in line.'

'As if I could.' Juno was scornful. Then she turned to Rachel again. 'You on holiday, Rachel? Or did this galoot invite you here?'

'Hey, I'm no galoot. I'm a pussycat,' Matt broke in before Rachel could answer her. 'Don't you be putting me down, woman.'

'Ain't no one could put you down, Brody,' declared Juno flatly. 'And you sure as hell ain't no pussycat, neither. A cougar, yeah? Or a jaguar. Anything else, you be kidding yourself.'

'I do that a lot,' replied Matt without rancour. His eyes flickered over Rachel again, and she was sure he could see the uncertainty in her eyes. But she still had no idea what he was thinking when he said casually, 'Well, you have to admit I have good taste.'

'Can't argue with that.' Juno was studying Rachel again with her dark assessing eyes. 'But you look out for this one. She looks fragile. Don't you go breaking her heart, you hear?'

Matt's lips twisted. 'I don't think I could,' he said drily, but Rachel had the uneasy feeling that he might be wrong. Though perhaps not in the way Juno anticipated. There was more than one way to tear a life apart.

'Anyway, I guess you've come for some of my Blue Mountain brew, yeah?'

'Yeah.' Matt nodded. 'Okay if we sit out on the deck?'

'Looks like you got it to yourselves,' agreed Juno. 'You take your ease. I'll see if Oscar's muffins are out of the oven yet.'

'From your lips to God's ear,' said Matt easily, before ushering Rachel ahead of him into the shadowy bar.

The bar was just a way to reach the deck outside. But even at this hour of the morning there were one or two men draped over the bar stools or leaning over a table, enjoying a game of chess. Rachel wondered how they could sit inside on such a lovely morning, but the effort to distract herself with commonplace musings didn't quite come off.

What had Juno meant? What other woman had come here with Matt? And how could she find out if it had been her mother?

Matt directed her to a table overlooking the street. It enabled them to enjoy the view of the harbour, and the flapping canopy overhead protected them from the worst excesses of the sun.

'Like it?' he asked, and Rachel dragged her mind from thoughts of her mother to give a little nod.

'It's very—very—'

'Quaint?' he suggested, arching dark brows, but Rachel shook her head.

'Atmospheric,' she decided firmly. 'It's the kind of place you can imagine pirates gathering to plan their next voyage.'

'Pirates, hmm?' Matt was sardonic. 'I assume you think I'd fit in very well?'

'If the cap fits,' said Rachel lightly, wondering how she could bring the conversation round to more personal matters. 'Juno seems to think you're a bit of a heartbreaker.' She paused. 'Are you?'

'That's for me to know and you to find out,' he remarked, picking up the salt cellar and weighing it in his strong hands. Long fingers shaped the shoulders of the small container, and Rachel felt that careless caress all the way down to her toes.

Then he looked up and found her watching him, and his eyes darkened to a shade of green only found at the bottom of the sea. 'What?' he asked. 'What are you thinking? I can feel your eyes undressing me. Or am I wrong?'

'You're wrong!'

He was always able to disconcert her, and she wished she dared ask him outright if he'd brought her mother here. That might disconcert him, but she couldn't guarantee it. Besides, she was such a wuss she didn't have the guts to do it.

'Okay.' While she'd been worrying over her options, Matt's eyes had remained on her. And now she could feel the hot colour rising up her cheeks. 'Would you like me to undress you instead? I'd enjoy that enormously. I might find an English rose tattooed on your butt.'

'You might not!'

Rachel stared at him angrily, and Matt gave her another considering look. 'You don't like tattoos?'

'I didn't say that.'

'Okay.' His eyes danced. 'I'll show you mine if you'll show me yours.'

Rachel pressed back against the slats of her chair. 'I've seen yours,' she said tightly, and Matt's lips quivered with amusement.

'So you have,' he agreed, sobering. 'Which doesn't seem fair, does it?'

Rachel couldn't look at him. In her mind's eye she could see the outline of the nighthawk very clearly. Indeed, she thought she'd glimpsed it earlier through the thin fabric of his shirt, its dark plumage unmistakable against his skin.

Once again the conversation had got away from her, and she was almost relieved when Juno returned with the coffee he'd ordered.

'Here we go,' she said, setting down two mugs of steaming black liquid. 'Now, I've brought you cream and sugar, Rachel. But I know Matt, here, likes it just the way it comes.'

'Don't I always?' remarked Matt lazily, and Rachel knew it was another comment that could be taken two ways.

'And Oscar's sent you each a pecan and maple syrup muffin,' Juno added, evidently used to his innuendos. She squeezed Rachel's shoulder. 'You try one of these, girl. It'll put a bit more flesh on those bones.'

'She doesn't need any more flesh on her bones.' Matt's protest was good-humoured. 'I think she's perfect the way she is.'

'Well, you be careful, girl.' Juno touched Rachel's shoulder again, almost in warning. 'When he tells you that you're perfect, he wants something. You can be sure of it.'

Rachel didn't have an answer to that, and she was almost as relieved when Juno went away again as she'd been when she'd arrived.

'Try the muffin,' Matt suggested, lifting his own and burying his strong white teeth in the soft sponge. 'Mmm, it's almost worth getting fat for.'

Rachel broke open the muffin in front of her, glad of something to do with her hands. And the smell almost made her salivate. She could easily forget why she'd invited him here. Crispy nuts, maple syrup, and rich fluffy sponge cake. Wonderful!

She nibbled on a corner, wondering how to begin. Then, after adding a slurp of cream to her coffee, she took a sip. As Matt had promised, it was delicious, the caffeine giving a much-needed boost to her psyche.

'Tell me about yourself.'

For a moment Rachel thought she must have conveyed the words by osmosis. But it wasn't she who'd spoken them. It was Matt.

'Tell me about Rachel Claiborne,' he said, watching the play of emotions crossing her face. 'Do you have a job in England? An occupation?'

'Well, I'm not a lady of leisure,' said Rachel tartly, before realising she was not going to get anywhere if she was offhand. 'I—well, I work for a newspaper.'

Matt regarded her with interest. 'You're a reporter?' he asked. 'What—are you some hot-shot columnist I should have heard of?'

Rachel had to smile then. Shaking her head, she said, 'Nothing so glamorous. I work for the *Chingford Herald*. It's just a local newspaper that mostly survives because of its advertising pages. I work in the advertising department, sometimes on the computer and sometimes on the phone, soliciting customers.'

'Soliciting, hey?' said Matt lazily, taking a mouthful of his coffee and savouring the taste. He grinned. 'Why am I not surprised?'

Rachel's lips tightened. 'Soliciting advertising,' she corrected him primly, and saw the way his lips twitched at her words. 'I'm actually quite good at it.'

'I believe you.' Matt allowed his eyes to drop to her mouth. 'Honestly, I do.'

He was teasing her, she knew, but Rachel was too tense to take it. 'No, you don't,' she retorted angrily. 'You're too busy trying to think of your next gibe. Let me guess: you think the only reason I got my job was because my boss fancied me.'

'No!' Matt groaned. 'I didn't say that. Boy, do you have some opinion of men! What happened? Did some cheap bastard seduce you and let you down?'

Rachel gasped, but when she would have jack-knifed out of the chair Matt's hand shot across the table to grasp her wrist. His fingers were surprisingly cool, but his grip was powerful. Rachel could feel its strength all the way up her arm.

'Calm down,' he demanded, and she was glad the deck was empty. 'What the hell else was I supposed to think when you react like crazy every time someone mentions your looks?' He shook his head. 'You *are* good to look at, Rachel. There, I've said it. So sue me. But I've known dozens of good-looking women who hold down responsible jobs purely on their own merit.'

Rachel felt foolish. 'I bet you have,' she muttered, in an effort to defend herself. But her awareness of him was now stirring like a fire in her belly. And that was bad.

'You have to have the last word, don't you?' he demanded harshly. 'But it may surprise you to know the world doesn't revolve around what you think.'

It wasn't easy, but somehow Rachel managed to drag her

wrist away. 'I never thought it did,' she denied, rubbing the feeling back into her arm. 'I'm sorry if I've offended you again, Mr Brody.' She thrust back her chair. 'I think it would be best for both of us if I just leave.'

'Rachel!'

She'd barely got to her feet before he moved into her path to stop her. Rachel turned then, desperately seeking for another way to get off the deck, and scurried towards the exit. She heard him coming after her, heard his feet thudding across the boards, so that when his arm snaked about her waist she panicked.

She was beating frantically at his arm when he hauled her back against him. 'Pack it in!' he exclaimed, his patience shredding. 'What do you think I'm going to do to you?'

'I don't know, do I?' she countered ridiculously, wondering what had happened to the cool, controlled individual she'd used to be. But as soon as he laid his hands on her all commonsense deserted her.

'Well, you're quite safe with me,' he told her grimly, the muscles of his chest and stomach hard against her quivering form. 'You're not irresistible, Rachel. Whatever you've been led to believe.'

Rachel let out a cry of protest. 'I don't believe I am irresistible. You—you just make me say things I don't mean.'

'And why is that?' he asked, bending his head close to her ear so she could hear the whispered words. 'Could it be because this is what *you* want? And you don't have the guts to ask for it yourself?'

Rachel's breathing constricted. 'Of course not.'

'Sure about that?' He deliberately pushed himself closer, so she could feel the unmistakable pressure against her bottom. 'Really?'

'I'm sure,' she said, but the words wobbled. She could feel his body stirring against her, and the knowledge was exhilarating and terrifying both at the same time.

She had to get away.

''Course, you know I'm enjoying this,' Matt went on roughly. And she suspected he wasn't quite as cool as he appeared when she heard an edge in his voice.

'I'm—sorry.' The words stuck in her throat. She was having to fight the urge to lean back against him. It was years since she'd allowed any man to touch her, and she had to remember her reasons for being here.

She glanced back over her shoulder, and any moisture there'd been in her mouth dried at the predatory gleam in his eyes. 'I—have to go,' she said, but she wondered if she really meant it. The feel of him, the smell of him, the raw male power of his nearness, was enveloping her in an unfamiliar haze of longing. And when his lips brushed her neck she felt as if her body was burning up.

But when his hands moved to her waist she sensed a certain ambivalence. Was he going to pull her even closer, or was he going to push her away? Her sudden intake of breath caused him to hesitate. And every nerve in her body tingled in anticipation of his kiss.

But he didn't kiss her. Instead, although his breath moistened her bare shoulder, it was his teeth that grazed her skin. He nibbled at her neck, pulled a pearl of soft skin into his mouth and suckled greedily. And wetness exploded between her legs as his tongue caressed her. It was as if he was possessing her, and she didn't want him to stop.

When he lifted his head, she felt almost dizzy with longing. She'd forgotten all about where she was, and that they were visible to anyone passing by on the harbour road.

But she didn't move. She wasn't sure her legs would support her if he released her. She just lay against his shoulder, panting, her breasts, her stomach, her thighs, all aching for him to go on.

It was Matt who spoke. 'You said something about leaving,' he muttered in a harsh voice, and Rachel needed several seconds to bring sanity back into focus again.

'I—I did,' she agreed at last. She forced herself to move away from him, knowing she'd made a terrible mistake. Thankfully, her legs did support her. But her whole body had stiffened with the callousness of his rejection.

'Yeah.'

As she turned, Matt ran an impatient hand down over his abdomen. She guessed he was making sure there was no evidence for her to see. 'Finish your coffee,' he said, striding away towards the bar behind them. 'Juno will be offended if you don't empty your cup.'

CHAPTER SIX

MATT drove back to the plantation house with Caleb clinging anxiously to his seat every time the Range Rover skirted the edge of the cliffs or came close to plunging down a ravine. The old man knew his employer was in a foul mood, and knew better than to complain about his driving.

But the breaths he kept sucking in eventually attracted Matt's attention, and he turned to Caleb with an impatient expression.

'What?' he demanded. 'Don't you trust me to get you back to Jaracoba in safety?'

'I wouldn't dream of saying such a thing, Mr Matthew,' said Caleb with dignity. And then, because he couldn't help himself after all, 'Please, sir. Keep your eyes on the road.'

Matt blew out an irritated breath, but he did as the man suggested and slowed the vehicle. He didn't want Caleb making some comment in his father's hearing when they got back to the house.

Nevertheless, he was cursing himself for the way he'd behaved at Juno's. It wasn't good enough to say Rachel had got under his skin—although she had. The truth was, he'd wanted to go a hell of a lot further than he'd permitted himself. And then only a massive effort of will had held him back.

He wasn't supposed to handle the merchandise, he thought bitterly. She was a guest at the hotel, and he'd had no right to touch her. Particularly knowing who she was. But his desire for her had got the better of him—or almost. He couldn't remember ever feeling such an attraction for a woman before.

Which was crazy, in the circumstances. She'd evidently come out here looking for her mother, and she wouldn't thank him for keeping information from her. But Sara had her own reasons for keeping their relationship a secret, and it wasn't really his place to interfere with her plans.

Nonetheless, it bugged him. It would be so much easier if Rachel knew who he was. But then, unless Sara changed her mind about being honest with her daughter, Rachel herself would want nothing to do with him. She would probably be horrified that he'd touched her at all.

Dammit!

He flung the vehicle through the gates of his family's plantation, barely skimming the stone posts as he accelerated past. An avenue of banana trees and coconut palms swept unnoticed by the open windows of the Range Rover, the fragrant scents of the orchids that grew beside the river as commonplace to him as the beautiful plantation house that stood at the end of the drive.

He brought the car to an abrupt halt beside the row of garages. Once these buildings had housed the carriages his ancestors had owned, and his father still retained a horse-drawn buggy that he occasionally used about the estate.

Caleb climbed out gratefully, and Matt pulled a wry face as he handed over the keys. 'I know, I know,' he said. 'You're glad to be back in one piece.'

Caleb's lined face broke into a grin. 'Fastest trip from town I ever made,' he replied humorously. 'Even your daddy never went faster than fifty miles an hour on those roads.'

Matt shrugged. 'What can I say? I'm a better driver than he is. Only don't tell him I told you.'

Leaving the old man laughing, Matt turned away from the garages to approach the house. Massive oak trees shaded the front of the building and Matt vaulted up the steps to the wraparound porch whose roof was supported by a dozen elegant pillars.

Double doors stood wide to the enormous hallway beyond, its polished boards gleaming from a thousand rubbings. Pale aqua-coloured walls created an atmosphere of lightness, the larger windows his father had had installed adding to its airy grace.

To the right of the hall double pocket doors gave access to a spacious morning room. And beyond this another door led into the library, which these days served as his father's study as well. To the left, a grand dining room led into a high-ceilinged sitting room, with his stepmother's music room at the back of the house.

Although it was already late afternoon, Matt made his way to his father's study. Giving a light tap on the door, he entered the room that Jacob Brody had made essentially his own. Although the stroke he'd had three months ago had left him partially paralysed down one side of his body, he was gradually regaining the use of his limbs.

Jacob was seated on a chaise-longue near the open window when Matt came into the room. He'd evidently been working, because his desk was covered with papers. But exhaustion had got the better of him, and he was taking a well-earned rest.

His eyes had been drooping when Matt entered the library, but they opened wide when they saw his son. 'You're late,' he said, attempting to sit up straight despite the weakness in his lower spine. 'Did you see Carlyle?'

'Yeah, I saw him.' Matt dropped into the chair at the other side of his father's desk. 'He's going to send the shipment out when the next supply boat arrives. That way it will go straight to Kingston and pick up the cargo ship from there.'

'Good, good.' His father nodded. 'What with one thing and another, I've been neglecting my duties.'

'You mean I have,' said Matt drily. 'And the girl's arrival is just another complication.'

'But I understand you find her quite fascinating,' remarked Jacob quietly.

'Ah. You've been talking to Amalie.' Not for the first time Matt resented his sister's interference. 'We met Rachel on the pier, after I'd checked out the *Bellefontaine*.'

'Rachel?' His father arched dark eyebrows, a mirror image of his son's.

'All right. Ms Claiborne, then,' said Matt sourly. 'A rose by any other name...'

'You think she's an English rose?'

Matt knew Jacob was only teasing him, but after this morning's encounter he couldn't respond in kind.

'Where is Amalie?' he asked instead, changing the subject. 'She's promised to be in for dinner. She wants to talk to me. About her allowance, I assume.'

'She's about here somewhere,' muttered his father vaguely. He still hadn't attuned himself to leaving the family finances to his son. 'Tell me about this girl. Sara's daughter. Is she as attractive as her mother?'

'She's nothing like Sara,' said Matt, not wanting to talk about the two women in the same breath. He flicked the papers lying on the desk. 'How are you getting on with your book?'

Jacob had been writing a history of the island for as long as Matt could remember. But since his stroke it had proved beneficial as a means to stimulate his attention. With Matt taking control of the running of the plantation, and the charter operation as well, Jacob had had plenty of time to review his notes.

The older man shrugged now. 'I haven't been in the mood for it today.'

Matt picked up a picture of a horse-drawn carriage that was to be included in the illustrations. 'That's a pity,' he said, putting one picture down and picking up another. 'These are really good.'

Jacob said nothing and, realising he couldn't avoid the subject entirely, Matt relented. 'You're not worrying about my relationship with Sara, are you?'

'Is there something I should worry about?' Jacob's eyes were shrewd. 'You care about her, don't you? How could I object to that?'

'I don't know.' Matt spoke broodingly. 'And Diana?' His stepmother had a right to an opinion. This was her home, too.

'Diana's far too busy arranging this year's music festival,' said her husband drily. 'In any case, she knows you have your own life to lead. We can't control who you choose to invite to Mango Key.'

Mango Key was Matt's own house that was situated on the other side of the plantation, near the ocean. He'd used to spend a lot of his time there. But since his father's stroke, and the increased responsibilities that had put upon him, he was spending more and more time at Jaracoba. Not that he minded. He loved the old house that would one day be his.

He scowled now. He'd been so sure he knew what he was doing. But since meeting Rachel the situation had changed. Why would she come out here, obviously looking for her mother, unless she had a very good reason? What had Sara told her family before making this trip to renew her acquaintance with him?

God knew, it was years since he'd seen her. He'd been a boy of barely nineteen when they'd first met in New York. He'd been in his first year at Princeton University, and his initial reaction to the older woman had been mixed.

Even today he wasn't sure if he really liked her. Loved her? Perhaps. But that was suspect, too. Sara had always been brittle, and now she was bitter. He had the feeling she thought the world owed her a living. That she resented the way her life had turned out.

Whereas Rachel...

But he didn't want to go there. He had no right thinking about Rachel, and she was certainly not someone he intended to discuss with her mother.

However, he would have to tell Sara that her daughter was on the island. That was the least he could do for either of them. He'd put off mentioning it to Sara for days, hoping—probably stupidly—the situation would resolve itself.

But it wasn't going to, and the sooner Rachel confronted her mother and left the island, hopefully taking Sara with her, the better it would be for all concerned. Whatever Sara said, she couldn't stay here.

His scowl deepened. He wouldn't want her to.

Rachel refused to look at the mark on her neck when she got back to the hotel. In retrospect, the scene had been so embarrassing the last thing she needed was a reminder of it.

But then, next morning, she looked into the bathroom mirror and saw it before she remembered what had happened. A dark stain against the still-pale skin of her throat, it was unmistakable. Anyone seeing it would know exactly what it was.

Which had probably been his intention, she thought, touching the mark with tentative fingers. It was hot and it was tender, and it wasn't going away.

If he'd bitten her anywhere else it wouldn't have been half so noticeable. With the slight tan she was acquiring it might have blended in. Not that he'd considered her feelings when he touched her. And the memory of his teeth, moving against her skin, could still bring a shiver of apprehension skimming down her spine.

Dear God, the man was dangerous. But she'd known that. He'd seduced her mother away from her father and now he was attempting to seduce her. He was a predator, as his tattoo announced, totally without conscience. And with all the savage grace of a tiger.

She blew out a breath and reached determinedly for her toothbrush. There was no use crying over spilt milk, as her grandmother used to say. She had to stop fretting about what had happened and concentrate on her reasons for being here. She still hadn't found her mother. That should be her primary concern.

The trouble was, when she'd had the opportunity to find out more about Matt she'd blown it. Her own lack of confidence in herself had ruined the chance she'd had.

If only she wasn't so aware of him. But she wasn't used to dealing with a man who could so easily use her own hang-ups against her. Let's face it, she thought disconsolately, she wasn't used to dealing with a man, period. Particularly not a man like him, who possessed such a raw sexual appeal.

With the mark on her neck blatantly proclaiming its origins, Rachel decided to leave her hair loose this morning. She could hardly cover up with a high-necked sweater, even if she'd brought one with her.

A cropped pink vest and the short pleated skirt she'd worn on her first morning on the island were hardly confidence building. But then, when she'd left England she hadn't known who—or what—she was going to dealing with.

Slipping wedge-heeled sandals onto her feet, she opened her door and stepped out onto the landing. It was still quite early, barely eight o'clock, but her body was taking longer to adjust to the five-hour time difference than she'd expected.

There was no one about. Apparently even her neighbours weren't up yet. She started towards the stairs and then halted abruptly. The double doors she'd seen Matt coming out of were just along the gallery. If it was his suite of rooms, might her mother be staying there?

It was worth a try, at least. If the doors were locked, so be it. But if they weren't…

They weren't. But when Rachel gripped the handle and opened one of the doors her disappointment was intense. Far from being the cosy love-nest she'd envisaged, beyond the doors was a large office, with printing machines and fax machines and filing cabinets, and a row of desks complete with computers.

Thankfully no one was about at the moment. It was obviously too early for the staff to be working. But she could imagine how embarrassed she'd have been if she'd had to confront a dozen curious faces.

Closing the door again, she hurried away, reversing her steps and heading back towards the stairs.

The lobby was blessedly familiar territory. 'Good morning, Ms Claiborne,' called the receptionist on duty, and Rachel acknowledged the greeting with an automatic smile. Evidently the staff were encouraged to remember the names of the visitors. Probably to promote an illusion of intimacy between themselves and the hotel guests.

Breakfast, thought Rachel, trying to focus on the morning's routine. Then another trip into town on the unlikely off-chance that she might run into her mother. And if that didn't work she was just going to have to ask Matt himself.

She wasn't looking forward to that event. He might not even come into the hotel today. Of course the taxi driver had said the Brodys owned most of the island, so surely it must be possible to get a phone number, at least?

'What in God's name are you doing here?'

Rachel had been heading towards the terrace restaurant when the irate yet absurdly familiar tones arrested her progress. With a feeling of disbelief, she turned on her heels to face the woman who was hurrying to catch up with her.

Her mother!

Who was barely recognisable, even so. In cream flared pants and a flowing smock, a long scarf in orange chiffon floating carelessly about her shoulders, Sara Claiborne looked much different from the woman who'd raised her. Her dark hair, which had been lightly threaded with grey, was now a startling shade of copper. She'd always been an attractive woman, but now her looks were enhanced with eyeshadow and mascara, her full lips painted a glossy shade of crimson.

She looked younger, too, but harder. Obviously she felt it was what she had to do to keep a man like Matt Brody.

Rachel felt sick. She'd wanted to find her mother, but not like this. And it was obvious that the older woman was decidedly less than pleased to see her.

'Mum...'

Rachel managed to get the word out, but when she went to give her mother a hug Sara Claiborne resisted the attempt.

'Come on,' she said shortly. 'What's going on here, Rachel? Oh, don't bother to answer that. I can see it in your face. Your father sent you. I should have known he wouldn't be able to keep his nose out of it.'

Rachel gasped. 'He was worried about you, Mum,' she whispered in protest, glancing anxiously around the lobby, sure that their conversation was being monitored by a dozen pairs of eyes.

'So he sent you here to spy on me, is that it?' Sara seemed to have no such worries. Her lips twisted. 'Really! That man is beyond belief.'

Rachel stared at her in astonishment. Then, with another glance about her, she said, 'Can we continue this in a less public place?'

'Why?' Sara was aggressive. 'I'm only speaking the truth.'

Rachel shook her head. If she'd ever pictured the scene where she found her mother, it had certainly been much different than this. Sara was in the wrong here; it was she who should be apologising to her husband. Instead of which she was accusing them of spying on her.

'Look, Mum—'

'No, *you* look.' Sara spoke tersely. 'I want you to go back to England, Rachel. I don't want you here. And as for the way you've been hanging about the Brodys…' She spoke contemptuously. 'I don't know what your game is, but you're not going to succeed.'

Rachel's jaw dropped. 'I haven't been "hanging about the Brodys" as you put it,' she protested. 'I've just been trying to find you, that's all.'

Her mother used her scarf to fan her flushed face, and then fixed her daughter with a piercing look. 'That's not what I hear from Matt.'

From Matt!

Rachel swallowed back the bile that rose into her throat at this accusation. She couldn't believe it. Matt had been reporting on her to her mother. Had Sara known she was here all this time without even bothering to pick up the phone?

'Well, you're wrong. *He's* wrong,' Rachel declared now, her cheeks burning at the insult. She was surprisingly near to tears, and that infuriated her. 'As for Daddy sending me here—what did you expect, Mum? You run off to the Caribbean to meet a man we don't know, without even telling us when you're coming back.'

'I may not come back.'

The words were spoken quietly enough, but their impact was terrifying. Sara's eyes left Rachel's face and drifted thoughtfully round the lobby. It was as if she was looking for someone, and for the first time Rachel wondered how she'd got to the hotel. Had Matt brought her? Her skin crawled at the prospect. She wanted desperately to escape to her room. She wanted to stay there until her mother had gone.

Which was ridiculous, in the circumstances. Dear God, she'd been trying to find her mother. And now she wished she hadn't. This woman was nothing like Sara Claiborne. She seemed totally self-absorbed, totally self-possessed. She was indifferent to her daughter's—and her husband's—feelings. It was as if the real Sara Claiborne had vanished and left this total stranger in her place.

Rachel caught her arm, unable to prevent herself from re-acting to such a bald statement. Besides, she wanted to be sure she had her mother's attention before she spoke.

'What do you mean?' she exclaimed. 'You might not come back? You have to. Surely you don't honestly believe you can stay here?'

'Why not?' Sara's eyes were distant now. 'I love this island.' She hesitated a moment, and then said slowly, 'I think the only times I've been really happy in my life is when I'm here.'

Rachel took an involuntary step backwards. 'You don't mean that.'

'Oh, I do.'

'But what about Daddy?' She bit back the words, *And me*, but they were tacitly implied just the same.

Her mother clicked her tongue. 'Oh, Ralph,' she said dismissively. 'You must know that your father and I have been having problems for some time.'

'No!'

'We have.' Sara's voice was flat. 'Ever since your father decided not to retire last year. I only agreed to sell the house and move into that poky apartment because he'd convinced me that it would give us more time and money to spend on holidays and travel. Instead of which he still goes off to work every morning, doing what he wants to do, and I don't even have a garden to distract me.'

Rachel blew out a breath. 'And have you told Daddy this?'

'Only a hundred times.' Sara's lips twisted. 'But he won't listen to me, so why should I listen to him?'

Rachel tried to think. Something else her mother had said suddenly came back to her. 'Have you been to St Antoine before?'

'When I was younger.' Sara was evasive. 'As I say, I love it here. I feel younger here.' Her eyes turned back to Rachel's. 'Is that such a bad thing?'

Rachel didn't know how to answer her. The trouble with being in the middle of something was that you could see both sides. But, whatever her mother said, she couldn't see any future for her with Matt Brody. Her hand strayed guiltily to the bite on her neck. Not when he didn't consider anyone but himself.

'Anyway...' Rachel had been quiet too long, and her mother was getting impatient. 'I don't really care what you think. I suggest you get on the phone and book yourself a flight back to England. If your ticket isn't viable I'll sub you, if you like. Just leave me alone to deal with things my way.'

'But, Mum—'

'And you can stop calling me *Mum* all the time. While I'm here, I'm Sara. That's what Matt calls me and I like it.'

Rachel didn't have an answer. And with a casual wave her mother swung on her heel and started towards the door.

'Don't blame me for wanting a life, Rachel,' she called back over her shoulder.

But Rachel had already turned away.

CHAPTER SEVEN

RACHEL spent the rest of the day in a state of raw confusion. There was no more need for her to go looking for her mother, but that was hardly a relief. And she still didn't know where Sara Claiborne was staying.

After drinking several cups of coffee in lieu of breakfast, she went up to her room and changed into a swimsuit and shorts. She couldn't go home, whatever her mother had said. Not yet. Not until she knew whether Sara was serious about staying here.

Going downstairs again, she bought a magazine at the hotel kiosk and settled herself in a lounge chair by the pool. She knew she ought to have rung her father, but she hadn't the first idea what she was going to say to him. It was really up to her mother to sort out her own problems, although the woman she'd met earlier didn't appear to have any that Rachel could see.

The whole situation was a nightmare. Watching holiday-makers splashing about in the pool, Rachel envied them their freedom. Her situation was so uncertain. And it was all Matt Brody's fault.

Despite her worries, the day passed remarkably quickly. She didn't eat any lunch. But she did buy two mugs of the delicious island coffee from the poolside bar.

She used the sunscreen she'd bought liberally, but her skin

still prickled. She knew she was overdoing it, but somehow sunburn seemed preferable to the torment of her thoughts.

She hadn't had a dip in the pool yet, so in the late afternoon she slipped off her shorts. Then, refusing to feel self-conscious, she crossed the tiled apron surrounding the pool and gazed down into the water.

The smell of the swimsuit reminded her irresistibly of Matt, and she wished she'd brought more than one suit with her. Despite rinsing it thoroughly when she'd got back from the beach, it still retained the tang of the sea.

The pool itself was almost empty. Most of the guests had gone up to their rooms to prepare for the evening ahead. Only two younger children were playing at the shallow end. Rachel had the deeper end to herself.

It looked very inviting and, taking a deep breath, she stretched out her arms and dived into the water. It wasn't exactly cold, but it wasn't warm either. The sun had only heated the surface. Deep down, she felt the chill sting her burning arms.

She came up gasping and swam swiftly from one side of the pool to the other. That felt better. The physical exertion warmed her limbs, and she swam back and forth a couple of times before returning to cling onto the rim.

She was breathless now. The unusual activity had robbed her of any strength. In addition to which she felt slightly dizzy. Probably because she'd had nothing to eat that day.

'Are you trying to kill yourself?'

The harsh masculine voice shouldn't have been familiar, but it was. Lifting her eyes, Rachel let her gaze travel up over formal suit trousers, that still couldn't quite disguise the impressive bulge between his legs, and an equally formal shirt and jacket, black on black. His tie was pearl-grey, the only splash of colour in his outfit. And, despite telling herself that she hated him, Rachel couldn't deny how completely stunning he looked.

'Well?'

He was waiting for her answer, and, dragging her eyes away from such perfection, she dug her nails into the tiles to ground her racing pulse.

'I don't see what business it is of yours, Mr Brody,' she said tightly, knowing the formality of her response would annoy him. 'I was having a swim, as it happens. As I'm sure you've seen for yourself.'

He didn't say anything for a moment, but she could feel his frustration coming off him in waves. And, in spite of her determination not to let him intimidate her, she had to look up at him. If only to assure herself that her words had found their mark.

'How long have you been out here?' he demanded. 'I assume you know your shoulders and arms are sunburned? It's probably just as well you can't see your face.'

'Why?'

'Guess.' He spoke impatiently. 'For God's sake, Rachel, I thought you had more sense.'

'Like my mother, you mean?'

Rachel couldn't resist the accusation, but if she'd expected any defence from him, she was disappointed.

'Let me help you out,' he said instead, bending and offering her his hand.

'I don't want to come out.' It was childish, she knew. Her limbs were already trembling with fatigue and she was beginning to shake.

'D'you want me to come in and get you?'

Rachel caught her breath. 'As if that's likely in that outfit,' she said scornfully. 'Go away, Matt. I don't need your help to get out of the pool.'

'Now.'

'Soon,' she compromised, even if the idea of letting go of the rim again filled her with apprehension.

'Now,' he insisted, and to her horror he took off his jacket.

He dropped it onto the lounge chair she'd been occupying and then returned to the pool-edge to pull off his shoes.

At once, Rachel realised he'd meant what he said when he'd threatened to come in and get her. 'Don't,' she cried, before he could remove the expensive loafers. 'All right. I'll get out. You don't have to continue the charade.'

'It's no charade,' retorted Matt bleakly, making no attempt to move away. 'Give me your hand.'

Rachel felt ridiculously mutinous. 'I don't need your assistance,' she insisted. But when she tried to press down on her hands to swing herself out of the pool there was no strength left in her arms.

Her fingers slipped off the ledge, and her arms flailed helplessly before she found herself sinking beneath the surface. And, because she wasn't prepared for the sudden submersion, her nose and mouth both filled with water.

Oh, God, she was drowning, she thought, momentarily panicking as the water closed over her head. Why couldn't she have acted sensibly and accepted Matt's help when he offered it? Could she do nothing right where he was concerned?

Her feet touched the bottom of the pool at that moment, and somehow she summoned all her strength and pushed upward again. And when she did Matt's hand grabbed one of her arms, bringing her to the surface.

He was kneeling on the side of the pool, and as she choked and gasped and tried to get her breath, he leaned into the water and caught her other arm. Then, getting to his feet, he hauled her unceremoniously out onto the side.

She heard him mutter something under his breath as she lay there panting. She could feel the weight of the water that was inside her, but she didn't have the energy to bring it up. Then, as if aware of her plight, Matt pressed a firm hand down on her stomach, rolling her onto her side as soon as she started regurgitating all the liquid she'd swallowed.

She coughed and coughed, fluid spilling out of her mouth

in such profusion she was sure she must have brought up every drop of liquid she'd swallowed that day. She felt hot, and shivery, and totally humiliated. Dear Lord, could this day get any worse?

Apparently it could.

Just as she was hoping he'd go away and let her die, he reached for his jacket and put it on. Then, to her horror, he bent and lifted her up into his arms.

'Your—your suit,' she croaked in protest, aware that she was soaking wet and probably smelling of vomit. But he didn't seem concerned.

'The suit will clean,' he said indifferently, and she had to admit she was grateful not to have to walk through the lobby. 'You need to get into the shower. You're burning up and shivering all at the same time.'

Rachel knew she ought to protest when he headed for the stairs. She cringed at the curious eyes that followed their progress, though she noticed no one attempted to say a word. It was Matt who said briefly, 'Bring a key, Toby,' to the porter, and she remembered she'd left her bag containing her key card and sunscreen beside the pool.

'Oughtn't I to—?'

'Later,' said Matt tersely, and she guessed he'd known exactly what she was going to say.

Toby overtook them on the landing, hurrying to open her door so that by the time Matt got there he could just carry her into her room. He nodded his thanks to the young porter and Toby said, 'No problem, Mr Brody,' before letting himself out again and closing the door.

Matt set her on her feet and nodded towards the bathroom. 'Do you think you can manage?' he asked, and Rachel wondered what he'd do if she said no.

'I think so,' she said instead. 'Um—thank you. And I'm sorry if I've ruined your suit. Let me at least pay for it to be dry-cleaned.'

'Get your shower,' said Matt, taking off his jacket again and looping it over one shoulder. She guessed he'd done it because the jacket was wet, and probably slimy, too. 'I'll arrange for you to have a meal sent up from Room Service.' And when she would have protested, he added, 'You need to eat. Something sweet, preferably. You've had a shock.'

She didn't argue. She didn't have the energy. And, as Matt seemed prepared to stay until she entered the bathroom, she decided to do as he said. She gave him a tentative smile before closing the door and locking it. He probably thought she was locking it against him, but he couldn't have been more wrong.

She ran the shower warm at first, and then slowly increased the pressure. He was right. The cascade of water did make her feel better, although she thought it might be some time before she entered a pool again. How could she have been so foolish? To risk the chance of sunstroke, and then wear herself out so completely she couldn't get out of the water.

She didn't let herself think what might have happened if Matt hadn't been around to save her. If he hadn't had the strength to haul her out. It was all too awful to imagine. Though she suspected she'd have nightmares for some time to come.

When she eventually emerged from the bathroom, wrapped in one of the white towelling bathrobes that was hung behind the bathroom door, she was feeling much better. Still shaken, but at least the shivery feeling had left her.

The mirror in the bathroom had told a different story, however. Her face, and what part of her arms and legs that had been exposed, were still red and angry-looking. Thank goodness her back hadn't been exposed. She might be able to sleep without too much discomfort.

Her eyes widened when she saw someone had entered the bedroom in her absence. The bag she'd left beside the pool was now lying on the bed. In addition, a serving cart had been left near the windows, its folding leaf extended and laid for one.

Her lips parting in surprise and anticipation, Rachel approached the cart. Silver domes hid a variety of dishes, including grilled fish and poached chicken, boiled green bananas and rice, baked crab and mixed salad. There were sweet things, too: sugary dumplings, a roasted pear torte, and ice cream flavoured with either mango or coconut.

A bottle of wine resided in a cooler, but Rachel doubted she'd drink any of that. The bottled water she found in a chilled compartment was much more appealing, and she drank almost a whole bottle before touching the food.

She tasted the fish and found it a little salty, but the poached chicken went smoothly down her throat. It was absolutely delicious. As, too, were the little dumplings. She tried one with a helping of mango ice cream, and was considering having another when someone knocked at her door.

She was reluctant to answer the door, looking as she did. What if it was her mother? What if Matt had informed Sara of her daughter's near drowning? What if the reason Matt had been so formally dressed was because he was taking her mother out to dinner?

She sighed. It could, of course, be the maid, come to collect the cart. And if she didn't answer would the girl let herself in, thus defeating any decision to ignore the knock?

Pushing back her chair, she padded across to the door and peered through the eyehole. Matt was standing outside, and her heart beat a rapid tattoo in her chest. Obviously she had him to thank for the meal she'd just enjoyed. But she doubted he'd arrived to collect the cart.

Although she was sure he couldn't see her, she stepped back automatically. 'Wh-who is it?' she called, and heard the impatient oath he uttered even through the door.

'You know who it is,' he told her shortly. 'You've been

eyeing me up for the last two minutes. Open the door, Rachel. I've brought some cream to treat your sunburn.'

'Oh!'

Rachel didn't hesitate any longer. Flicking the latch, she opened the door a few inches, keeping mostly out of sight. Matt had changed his clothes, she saw. He was now wearing casual drawstring sweats and a white tee shirt. And, judging by the drops of water sparkling on his hair, he'd had a shower, too.

'Thanks for dinner,' she said, attempting to keep her eyes on the jar of cream in his hand and not on the wedge of brown skin exposed by the low-slung pants. 'I—is that the cream?'

Matt glanced down at the jar. Then up again to meet her nervous eyes. 'Yeah,' he said without expression. 'May I come in?'

Rachel expelled an uneven breath. 'You—er—you were going out for dinner, weren't you?' she ventured, which was hardly an answer. 'I suppose I spoiled your plans.'

'You could say that,' agreed Matt, his eyes moving beyond her. 'Are you going to invite me in, or have you already got company?'

Rachel gasped. 'As if!'

'So?'

'I'm not dressed.'

'I can see that.'

'Oh, well—' Deciding she was as adequately clothed as she'd been that afternoon, Rachel stepped away from the door. 'I suppose you can come in.' How could she refuse when he'd practically saved her life?

He came into the room, immediately making it seem smaller. She hadn't noticed that phenomenon earlier, but then she'd been too shocked to notice much beyond the relief of knowing she was safe.

He glanced about him, his eyes taking in the remains of

the meal she'd consumed, his brows arching at the unopened bottle of Chablis. Then he closed the door behind him, leaning back against it as his eyes turned back to hers.

'I—er—I liked the chicken,' she said hurriedly, desperate for something to say to normalise the situation. 'And—and the ice cream. It was scrummy.'

'Scrummy?' His lips twitched. 'I don't think I've heard that word before. I assume it means you enjoyed it, too?'

'Mmm.' Rachel found herself wrapping the folds of the bathrobe closer about her. 'I know I thanked you before for—you know—saving my life and all, but I want you to know I do appreciate what you did.'

'Particularly as you were such a prickly little cat?' suggested Matt drily, straightening away from the door. 'But I can't take credit for saving your life. You'd have got out of there somehow. The human need for survival's a powerful thing.'

'All the same...'

'All the same, you're grateful I was there.' Matt pulled a wry face. 'But not soon enough to save you from burning that delicate skin.'

Did he really think she had delicate skin?

Rachel found the prospect totally intriguing, before commonsense surfaced again. But she couldn't help being irresistibly aware of the intimacy of him being here, in her room. He was far too attractive. Far too close.

In an effort to distract herself, she pointed to the jar he was holding. 'And that's the cream?'

'You asked me that before,' Matt reminded her mildly. 'And, yes, once again, this is the cream. It's a special recipe that my grandmother used when she first came to the island. She was pale-skinned, too, and in those days there were no handy pharmacies with a dozen prescription remedies on hand.'

Rachel put out her and. 'What is it?'

'That would be telling.' Matt looked at the jar, but he didn't give it to her. 'It contains lanolin and witch hazel, and cocoa butter, and a few other ingredients. The housekeeper makes it up whenever it's needed.'

'Well—thank you.' Rachel wished he would just give her the cream and leave. 'I'll be glad to use it.'

'And how to you propose to put it on your shoulders?' Matt demanded tersely. 'Loosen your robe. I'll do it for you.'

'No, I—'

'For God's sake, stop behaving as if a man has never seen you naked before,' he grated. 'I'm only offering to treat your shoulders. You can do the rest yourself.'

Rachel swallowed. She wondered what he would say if she told him that no man had ever seen her naked. Well, not since she was a baby, of course. But pride won out over honesty. She'd embarrassed herself enough as it was.

'Well—all right,' she murmured at last. 'Where do you want me to sit?'

CHAPTER EIGHT

MATT wondered what she'd say if he told her. But he reminded himself that he was here for one purpose and one purpose only: to try and ease her sunburn.

The fact that it was burning him up, too, was not her problem.

'Sit on the side of the bed,' he said a little shortly, watching as she carefully eased the collar of the robe down around her upper arms. He knew she was no more exposed than she would have been in an off-the-shoulder evening gown, but the sight of her red skin caused a tightening in his gut.

She looked so fragile, so vulnerable. He wished he could take the pain from her. But his own skin would never burn like this.

Unscrewing the jar, he hesitated a moment and then sat down behind her. Now the heat of her skin rose irresistibly to his nose. A feminine scent mingled a flowery fragrance with warm perspiration, an essence that he found utterly desirable.

Impatient with his reactions, Matt scooped a smear of the ointment onto his fingers. Then, trying to be gentle, he applied it liberally over her reddened skin. She flinched, as he'd expected, but she seemed to steel herself to suffer his attention. Matt couldn't be sure if it was the sunburn cream she was steeling herself against or him.

He could smell the cream now. The delicious aroma of

cocoa butter heightened his awareness of her tender flesh. His gentle massage became a caress, took pleasure in exploring the bones and angles of her shoulders. But his fingers were now pressing far too firmly into her sensitive skin.

He heard her catch her breath, realised instantly what he was doing. And was disgusted with himself for the way he'd behaved. But, dammit, touching her like this was the purest kind of torment he could imagine. She was so soft, so delicate. He couldn't help himself; he wanted more.

His whole body was suddenly charged with tension. As she allowed the folds of the bathrobe to slip lower, he was gifted with a glimpse of the creamy slopes of her breasts. And his eyes were caught by the mark he'd put upon her that day at Juno's. His body stiffened, tightened, grew hard without any volition on his part.

Seeing the bite, he realised what a mistake he'd made in coming here, in thinking he could ignore the connection between them. Rachel was aware of it. That was why she'd been so reluctant to let him into her room. And now here he was, having the kind of thoughts that should have been left outside the door.

With a grim determination he finished his task and screwed the cap back onto the jar. Then, rubbing his hands together, he removed the last vestiges of the cream. She could manage the rest herself, he thought. He certainly couldn't trust himself to touch her again.

Yet he didn't move. For a few seconds he just sat there, putting off the moment when he would have to leave. Then, unable to prevent himself, he leant towards her and blew gently into her ear.

Her head positively spun round, her eyes registering her shock at the unexpected coolness of his breath. 'Did you—?' She broke off abruptly, obviously seeing her answer in his expression. 'Please—don't,' she whispered huskily, but Matt's eyes were on her mouth.

She had such a sensual mouth, he thought, wide and soft and vulnerable. Doubly so as she struggled to maintain some kind of control over the situation.

'Don't what?' he asked unforgivably. As if he didn't know exactly what she meant. He lifted his hand and allowed one finger to stroke down the side of her neck and across her shoulder. 'Doesn't this feel better? Now that the cream has had a chance to do its work?'

'Matt, please…'

'Let me move your hair out of the way,' he said, taking no notice of her protest. 'We don't want to get it greasy, do we?'

Her hair was still damp from her shower, and it clung silkily to his fingers as he lifted a handful to his face. He opened his mouth and allowed the damp strands to invade his lips, glorying in its softness. And, although he was sure she was desperate to move, his sensuous action forced her to stay where she was.

'Matt…'

'Mmm?'

But Matt wasn't really listening to her. Using his free hand, he tugged the bathrobe lower. And as he did so one hard rosy peak emerged proudly from the cloth. Rachel gasped, and would have quickly covered herself again, but Matt wouldn't let her. Instincts as old as time had him firmly in their grip.

When he released her hair, it tumbled unheeded about her shoulders, and Matt allowed his hands to slide smoothly down her neck. His thumbs brushed her ears, felt the pulse beating rapidly in its hollow, and gave in to the urge to follow a path that led unerringly to her breasts.

Common sense and decency seemed to have deserted him. He hadn't intended to touch her, he told himself, but he couldn't let her go. Not yet. Not while her nipples swelled against his palms and he could hear the uneven tenor of her breathing. And she didn't try to stop him except to say in a shaken voice, 'We shouldn't.'

And, God, Matt knew that. Knew he was probably damning his soul for all eternity by taking advantage of her susceptibility. She was fragile at present, weak and breakable. And this was definitely not a great idea.

But it was useless telling himself this when she was so desirable. He already knew how good she tasted, and he badly wanted to taste her again. But not just her soft skin, all of her. Her palms, the backs of her knees, and most particularly that sensitive place between her legs.

Feeling his own body trembling, he half turned her to face him, only to find her eyes were closed. But she didn't resist when his thumb tugged her lips apart and invaded her sweetness. Or when he bent his head and covered her mouth with his own.

He pushed his hands into her hair, angling her face so he could deepen the kiss, allowing his tongue to push into her mouth. Her eyes opened then, but they were soft and languorous. His tongue sank deeper and her breasts were crushed sweetly against his chest.

Her hand rose to clutch the neck of his tee shirt. Soft fingers invaded his collar, curled with unexpected eagerness into his hair.

'You want this?' he breathed against her neck, his own breathing harsh and staccato.

'I want you,' she admitted huskily, her tongue a sexual invitation, and Matt felt any lingering doubts spinning away.

It was easy enough to propel her back on the bed, to loosen her robe and tug the sides apart. There was a moment when he thought she might stop him. Her back arched upward off the quilt, but then subsided again.

Matt eased himself beside her, bending to flick one of those delicious nipples with his tongue. She sucked in a breath and he was struck by how sensitive she was. She was so responsive. He'd never met a woman like her before.

He couldn't help himself. His eyes drifted down over her body. She lay there, legs pressed tightly together, gazing up at him with wide trusting eyes. She was definitely a blonde, he noticed, and then put such thoughts aside. His interest went far beyond the colour of her hair.

She was amazing, he thought. Full breasts, slim and yet rounded hips, long shapely legs. Legs he could already imagine wound around him. And a waist he could span with his two hands.

'You're beautiful,' he said a little thickly, trailing wet kisses across the slight mound of her stomach. He felt her flinch again when he explored her navel with his tongue, and was briefly diverted. She was either very tense or very nervous. He knew she'd had a tough day, but he wanted her to relax.

Then she said, 'Oh, please...' and Matt gave a soft laugh as he looked down at her.

'I intend to,' he assured her huskily. 'Do you mean you or me?'

Rachel shook her head and he returned his attention to her breasts, lifting them into his hands with an unexpected sense of possession. Then he bent to curl his tongue about their swollen peaks.

When he pulled one into his mouth and sucked strongly, he heard her give a soft whimper. But it wasn't a whimper of pain, it was one of pleasure.

'You like that?' he asked, lifting his head and looking at her through his lashes.

'I—like,' she got out unsteadily, her hands reaching for his shoulders, her nails digging almost painfully into his flesh.

Matt expelled a hoarse breath. God, he wondered incredulously, was this woman for real or what? He couldn't ever remember wanting a woman so badly. His erection was almost painful, and he was so glad he'd changed into the loose-fitting sweats.

His hands left her breasts to curve possessively over her hips. He raised one of her legs to bestow a lingering kiss behind her knee and the unmistakable scent of her arousal rose hotly to his nostrils. His hand slid along her thigh, cupped the provocative curve of her bottom, found her damp cleft and allowed his fingers to probe the honeyed curls of her mound...

And then someone knocked at the door.

'Dammit!'

Matt swore more forcefully under his breath, but there was no way he could ignore the summons. The door was closed, but it wasn't locked. And besides, all the housekeeping staff had keys.

His dark eyes met Rachel's startled ones, but she was already wrapping her robe about her, drawing up her legs and huddling back against the headboard behind her. It was obvious what she was thinking; she was probably grateful for the interruption. But Matt had to stifle his frustration as he pushed himself abruptly to his feet.

Crossing to the door, he swung it open with scarcely concealed impatience. It was one of the maids, as he'd suspected, but her eyes widened anxiously when she saw her employer.

'I—er—I've come to turn down the bed,' she said, and Matt was glad his bulk blocked her curious view.

'Thank you, but Ms Claiborne doesn't require your services this evening,' he said.

'Perhaps some towels?' the girl suggested, and Matt wondered if she knew how dangerously she was pushing her luck.

'Nothing,' he said shortly, his eyes brooking no argument, and with another futile attempt to see beyond him the maid turned regretfully away.

Matt closed the door, but for a moment he didn't turn

to look at Rachel. Bracing his hands against the panels, he knew without asking that the maid's intrusion had destroyed any intimacy between them. They were back to square one, and perhaps it was just as well, he thought broodingly. This could have been a mistake. And one he might not be able to dismiss.

Steeling his features, he turned, and found she had left the bed to stand beside the windows. The bathrobe was now securely in place again, her hair twisted into a single coil at her nape.

'You heard that?' he said, and she gave him a brittle little nod over her shoulder.

'Perfect timing,' she said tightly. 'Are you leaving now?'

Matt's smile was bitter. 'Is there any point in my staying?'

Rachel shook her head. 'Probably not.'

'That's what I thought.' Matt picked up the jar of cream from the bed and dropped it onto her night table. 'Don't forget to put some of this on your arms and legs. However they feel now, they will feel worse in the morning.'

'Thank you.'

'My pleasure.' Matt's lips twisted and he turned towards the door. 'And it has been,' he added, disregarding the ache of thwarted arousal. 'Get a good night's rest. It's been a long day.'

Rachel did not sleep well.

As soon as Matt had gone, she'd hurried across the room and locked the door. Not that she expected to be disturbed again. But the action offered a sense of security she'd totally lost.

And, despite being exhausted after all the physical and emotional stimulus of the day, she couldn't rest. She tossed and turned for hours, wondering what she'd have done if the maid hadn't interrupted them. What had she been thinking?

Had she even been thinking? Or had Matt's demands on her senses reduced her brain to a quivering lump of mush?

Perhaps.

She knew she'd totally forgotten her reasons for making this journey. She hadn't thought about her mother, or her father, or what any relationship she might have with Matt would do to them.

Particularly her mother, she conceded, half guiltily, aware that, however reprehensible her mother's behaviour might have been, she evidently cared about Matt. As evidence: the fact that she'd virtually ordered Rachel to leave the island. It wasn't her fault that her daughter was as susceptible to the man as she had been herself.

Rachel's only excuse was that the events of the day had left her reeling. And the gratitude she'd felt towards Matt had made her vulnerable in a way she'd never been before. How was she expected to understand feelings that went beyond anything she'd ever experienced? How could she cope with a man who was as unpredictable as he was beautiful?

But that was too simple an explanation for what had occurred. She'd always been able to control her emotions in the past, so why couldn't she control them now? Something had changed. Something she dared not examine. Since meeting Matt, common sense seemed to have deserted her.

She'd wanted him. There was no doubt about that. For the first time in her life she'd understood the emotional needs that had so far been denied to her. She'd wanted to give herself to him. She hadn't cared about losing control, or losing her virginity. Those things had meant nothing at that moment. She'd wanted to take what he was offering and run with it, to find out at last what she'd been missing all these years.

Or not.

She was fully aware that the experience might not live up to her expectations. When she was at school, she'd decided she wasn't a sexual person at all. Despite her appearance—and the fact that boys thought she must be gagging for it—Rachel had had no difficulty in keeping amorous youths at bay.

Unfortunately, as she'd grown older she'd realised that those early experiences had helped to establish the pattern of her life. She'd had male friends, but she'd never allowed any of them to get close to her. She'd enjoyed their company, their conversation, but as soon as some commitment was needed Rachel had quickly moved on.

And as for love…

How arrogant she'd been, she thought as she lay sleepless, pummelling her pillow continuously, trying to find a comfortable place to lay her head. She'd been foolish to make such a sweeping assumption about her future. Just because she'd never met a man she wanted to go to bed with, it didn't mean he wasn't out there somewhere.

Someone like Matt…

She was up and dressed early the next morning. Her hair, untamed after her shower the night before, now curled riotously to her shoulders. There were lines around her eyes, not surprisingly after the restless night she'd spent, and her lips looked faintly bruised from Matt's sensual mouth.

She touched her lips with fingers that trembled slightly. But then, seeing the weakness, she dragged her hand away. Okay, she was a virgin, but thankfully Matt didn't know that. And if she did see him today she was going to have to pretend he hadn't just blown her mind.

She didn't think she would see him, though. He had no doubt had second thoughts about what had so nearly happened last night, just as she had. She recalled how he'd stood and stared at the door after the maid had departed. It was as if he'd been steeling himself to tell her he was leaving, too.

She shouldn't have been surprised. Dear God, his involvement with her had obviously gone far further than he'd intended. It was all right telling herself that she was doing it for her father, but was she? How far was she prepared to go to save her parents' marriage?

After brushing her hair and securing it with a scrunchie, she examined her arms and legs. The skin still looked a bit angry, but the cream Matt had given her had definitely helped. The burning sensation had almost completely gone.

Then she stepped out onto her balcony, trying to regain the optimism she'd felt when she first arrived on the island. The warmth, the atmosphere, the promise of another beautiful day, were appealing. If only she could concentrate on why she was really here.

Below her, the seductive beauty of the pool mocked her reasoning. It held so many connotations, not least the recollection of what had happened the night before in this room. It was impossible to escape those memories. She had the feeling they'd stay with her for the rest of her life.

Her stomach clenched. If she did see Matt again, how was she going to face him? Recalling the way he'd seen her, on the bed behind her, she felt sick. He might have been just as involved as she had, but he hadn't been naked. Somehow that made everything worse from her point of view.

Still, it was just as well he had had his clothes on when the maid had knocked at the door. She had little doubt that their being together, alone, in her room had not gone unremarked by his staff. She could only hope that the fact that Matt had practically followed the woman downstairs would silence the gossips. Was there a chance that her mother might hear about it, too?

Oh, God!

Thinking about her mother aroused other concerns. She was fairly sure Sara Claiborne would contact the hotel this morning, just to make sure that Rachel had checked out. And when she found she hadn't, could Rachel expect another visit? And if she did appear, what was Rachel going to say?

She decided to wear a simple chemise dress in island cotton. It was navy, with purple flowers, and she'd bought it on her first trip into town when she'd realised that her wardrobe was fairly limited. The colours helped to tone down her sunburned arms.

She spent a few minutes tidying her room before going down for breakfast. She had no desire to be the first person in the restaurant, particularly as she had no appetite to speak of. But she needed to think, to marshal her defences, just in case her mother turned up again. And she'd do that so much better, she thought, with a couple of cups of strong black coffee inside her.

Thankfully, there were several other guests already occupying the tables on the patio. One or two of them acknowledged Rachel, and she managed a friendly wave of recognition. Although it was only a little after eight, people did seem to get up earlier here. Probably to get out and about before the heat of the day sucked all their energy.

She'd drunk three cups of coffee and managed to swallow half an English muffin when someone spoke to her.

It was a male voice, and she instantly thought of Matt. But the young man standing beside her table was a stranger. Well, not a complete stranger, she admitted honestly. He and his partner were two of the people who'd waved to her when she'd first come down.

'Hi,' he said, putting a hand on the back of the chair opposite, evidently waiting for an invitation to sit down.

But Rachel didn't respond to his silent question. She merely raised her face to his and forced a small smile. 'Hi,' she returned, and then dropped her eyes to her plate again, in the hope that he'd get the message. He was already one of a couple. So what was he doing talking to her?

He didn't move away. Instead, he said, 'Are you enjoying your holiday?'

Rachel was tempted to tell him she wasn't on holiday,

exactly, but that would require too much explanation. 'Very much,' she replied, in what she hoped was a quelling tone. Then, pushing back her chair she got purposefully to her feet.

She was preparing to give him another smile and move away, but he blocked her exit.

'You're on your own, aren't you?' he persisted. 'Luce and I saw you sitting by the pool yesterday. We wondered if you'd like to join us for the morning. We've booked one of those boat trips that take you to a secluded cove where you can swim and snorkel. They offer you a picnic on the beach, as well.'

Rachel immediately felt guilty. Was she so conceited that she'd mistaken a friendly gesture for a pass?

'I—well, that's very kind of you—'

'If you've got something else planned, then that's okay.'

Had she?

The answer was a definite no. Short of making another trip into town to try and find out where her mother was staying, she had no plans. There was nothing to stop her from joining them, and it might be fun.

'I don't have anything else planned,' she admitted, glancing across the patio to where his partner was waiting. The girl waved, and any lingering doubts Rachel might have had faded away. 'Thank you. I'd be happy to join you. What time are you leaving?'

'About nine.' The man grinned. 'My name's Mark Douglas, by the way. And that's my wife, Lucy.'

'Oh—well, I'm Rachel Claiborne.' Rachel gave the girl another awkward wave. 'I'll meet you in the lobby, right? I just need to collect a few things from my room.'

Most particularly sunscreen, she thought. She wasn't at all sure that going out in the sun again was the most sensible thing to do.

But it was only for the morning...

'Great.'

Mark looked pleased, and although Rachel knew she had no reason to feel apprehensive she hoped she wasn't making a big mistake. And not just about going out in the sun, she thought anxiously. But, for heaven's sake, they were going on a boat with a lot of other people. And his wife didn't look the type to allow her husband to play around.

CHAPTER NINE

TO BEGIN with, Rachel enjoyed the outing.

It was so good to be with people who knew nothing about her. Who accepted her story that she'd planned to come on holiday with a girlfriend, but the friend had been taken ill at the last moment and been unable to come.

And Mark and Lucy were a nice couple. Mark did most of the talking, but Lucy seemed not to mind. A placid girl, with long dark hair and pretty features, she seemed quite content to leave everything to him.

It was only when her husband went to talk to the skipper of the vessel that she confided to Rachel that they were on their honeymoon. She became quite animated when she described the elaborate wedding dress she'd worn.

They anchored off a small cove, and most of the young people on board dived into the water and swam to the beach. The older members of the party were ferried ashore in a dinghy. Then time was allotted for swimming and snorkelling before a picnic lunch was served.

The food wasn't great, but the scenery was spectacular. In any case, Rachel wasn't hungry. Despite her determination to leave her problems behind her, she couldn't help thinking about her father. What was she going to tell him the next time she called?

Chewing on a skewer of jerk chicken and pimento, she wondered what Matt was doing today. Probably making up with her mother, she mused ruefully. She hoped he wouldn't bring Sara to the hotel.

So far, they hadn't actually discussed his association with her mother. She would find it hard—no, make that *impossible*—to bring the subject up. How could she ask him his intentions towards the other woman when she herself was in such an impossible situation?

They sailed back into the harbour soon after three o'clock. It was later than Rachel had expected, and she could feel her skin prickling with the heat. She had taken precautions, covering her arms and legs with sunscreen as soon as she came out of the water, staying under the parasols the ferry company had provided while she ate her lunch. But the sun was relentless.

Still, it had been a nice day. It had kept her away from the hotel for over six hours and that was good.

It was only as they were driving back to the hotel that Rachel was forced to review her opinion of Mark Douglas. He'd hired a buggy for the duration of their stay on the island, and it was this they'd used that morning to get down to the quay.

Rachel had been seated in the back, of course, but on the return journey Lucy had insisted that she should take the front seat beside Mark.

'It's only fair,' she said easily. 'I'm quite happy to sit in the back.'

Rachel would have been quite happy to sit in the back, too. But it would have been churlish to refuse the young woman's offer.

So, despite some misgivings, she climbed into the front of the buggy, aware that the beach wrap she'd had to put on over her wet swimsuit clung to her body like a second skin.

The first half of the journey passed without incident. It wasn't far from the harbour to the hotel. And, although it was hot, the breeze generated by the open-topped vehicle was welcome relief.

Rachel was happily anticipating the shower she intended to take as soon as they got back when Mark's hand suddenly landed on her bare thigh.

She was horrified. What in God's name was he thinking? His new wife was sitting happily behind them, totally unaware of what was going on.

Sucking in a startled breath, she pushed his hand away, her eyes turning angrily in his direction. 'Do you mind?' she mouthed, not wanting to upset Lucy. She was half inclined to ask him to pull over so she could get out.

'Ooh, sorry!'

If Mark thought the leer of apology he cast in her direction was sufficient, he was very much mistaken. Rachel was fuming, wishing desperately that she'd refused his invitation in the first place.

'I'm not used to driving a stick shift,' he continued, gripping the gearstick ostentatiously. As if he expected her to believe he'd made a mistake.

'What's wrong?'

Lucy had evidently picked up the tail-end of this exchange. But Mark wasn't about to let Rachel give her an explanation.

'Oh, it was just me, bumping Rachel's leg with the gearstick,' he said blandly. 'Sorry about that, Rachel. You've got such long legs, I must be feeling confined.'

Rachel's lips tightened. 'No problem,' she said, hoping he didn't think she bought that apology. She couldn't wait to get out of the buggy.

At the hotel, Lucy got out with obvious enthusiasm. 'Oh, I have enjoyed today,' she said happily. 'You'll have to come with us again, Rachel. I know we'd both love to have you.'

Rachel's smile was forced, but she could hardly blame Lucy

for her husband's crassness. 'Thank you for asking me,' she said politely. 'Would you pass me my bag?'

'I'll get it.' Mark jumped out of the buggy at once, folding the seat forward to reach into the back. 'You go ahead, Luce,' he said. 'I'm going to have myself a beer before I get my shower. You can use the bathroom first.'

'Oh, okay.' Lucy was clearly used to this arrangement. 'See you tomorrow, Rachel,' she called, waving her hand as she walked into the hotel.

I don't think so, thought Rachel, turning to take her rucksack from Mark with every intention of following her. But it was a shame that Mark's behaviour had spoilt the day.

However, he kept a firm hold on her bag, even after his wife was out of sight. 'Why don't we both have a drink together?' he suggested silkily. 'I'm sure you must be ready for something stronger than root beer.'

Rachel caught her breath. 'No, thank you.'

'Oh, come on.' Mark narrowed his eyes. 'I know you like me. I've seen you watching me when you thought Luce wasn't looking. I'm sure she bought all that girlish outrage in the buggy, but you don't have to pretend now. She's gone, babe. You can be yourself.'

Rachel could hardly speak. She *was* outraged. How dared he think she would be prepared to go anywhere with him?

'Just give me my bag,' she said, keeping her tone neutral. 'I want to go up to my room.'

'Why don't you show me your room?' he proposed eagerly. 'Don't be coy, babe. We're both adults. You know I can give you a good time.'

Rachel's gaze was unbelieving. 'You've got to be joking,' she exclaimed, her anger showing. 'Please—give me my bag. I don't want to have to report you to the staff.'

'You wouldn't do that.' He was so smug Rachel wanted to slap him. 'Luce likes you. How do you think she'll feel when

I tell her you've been coming on to me? And I warn you, babe, it's not you she'll believe.'

'Don't call me babe!'

It was all Rachel could think to say. This shouldn't be happening, she thought helplessly. She'd done nothing, absolutely nothing, to encourage him to think—

'Is something wrong here?'

The voice was so memorable. It shouldn't have been, but it was. Rachel turned her head and saw Matt Brody approaching them, his expression revealing nothing of his thoughts.

He seemed so painfully familiar. Although she'd only known him for a few days, she already felt as if he'd always been part of her life. In dark linen pants and a black body shirt, he looked both powerful and intimidating. And when he met her eyes there was so much sexual chemistry in his gaze that she felt its kindling deep inside her.

It was Mark who spoke first. 'No, Mr Brody, nothing's wrong.' He handed Rachel her bag. 'Rachel joined Luce and me on one of those picnic cruises around the island, and we were just saying we'll have to do it again.' His eyes turned to Rachel. 'Isn't that right?'

Rachel pressed her lips together for a moment. Then she said tightly, 'That's right.'

'Maybe tomorrow, hmm?' Mark was persistent. 'I'll get Luce to give you a ring in the morning. Or perhaps you'd like to join us for dinner tonight?'

'No, thanks.'

Somehow Rachel got the words out, but inside she badly wanted to scream. Did Matt believe him? Was that speculative look he was wearing a signal that he suspected neither of them was telling the truth?

'Excuse me…'

Rachel couldn't take any more. Uncaring what either of them thought of her, she ducked her head and hurried across the forecourt and into the hotel. Her flip-flops smacked against the tiles, attracting attention she could very well do without. But at last she reached the stairs and climbed quickly up to her room.

Sagging back against the door, she breathed a sigh of relief. Dear God, what an awful end to what had been a fairly pleasant day. And she didn't kid herself that Mark's pursuit of her was over. She'd met men like him before, and she knew it would take more than one refusal to put him down.

The phone rang as she was going into the bathroom. Her father, she thought wearily. He'd probably been trying to reach her all day. If she told him what she'd been doing he'd assume she was wasting her time.

She couldn't ignore it, however, and, picking up the receiver, she said, 'Yes?'

'Rachel?'

It wasn't her father. Her legs gave out on her and she had to sit down on the bed.

'Yes,' she said, unable to think of any reason Matt might be calling her.

'Have you any plans for dinner?'

Plans? Rachel pulled a wry face. How could she have any plans?

And then understanding came to her. This was Matt's way of finding out if she'd really meant what she said when she'd refused Mark's invitation.

Indignation souring her voice, she said tartly, 'No. I have no plans. I intend to order a meal from Room Service. Then I'm going to have an early night.'

'Are you tired?'

Matt sounded sympathetic, but she resented his enquiry even so. 'No, I'm not tired. And nor am I having a secret tryst with Mark Douglas. I assume that's what you're getting at, but the man's a moron. I wish I didn't have to see him again.'

'Yeah.' Matt sounded amused. Did he believe her? 'That was my impression, too. I hope you don't mind, I told him we were seeing one another. I let him think we'd had a disagreement, and that was why you were on your own.'

Rachel blew out a breath. 'You didn't!'

'I did.' Matt waited a beat. 'Did I do wrong?'

'Heavens, no!' Rachel's relief was heartfelt. 'I didn't know how I was going to convince him to leave me alone.'

'Yeah, I got the picture.' Matt's acceptance was such a godsend Rachel wanted to cry. 'So, if you've no plans and you're not tired, how about having dinner with me?'

Rachel sniffed. 'You don't have to do this, you know. I mean—I'm sure Mark's a coward. Now that you've sort of—staked your claim, he probably won't bother me again.'

'I know that.' Matt's tone was easy. 'But I want to. Are you still set on having an early night?'

Rachel's heart was beating so fast she was sure he must be able to hear it. Dear Lord, after last night she'd been sure Matt would never want to see her again. And that was without the guilt she felt over both her mother and her father. What sense was there in pursuing this relationship when it could only end in tears?

'I—what time were you thinking of having dinner?' she ventured, despising herself for even considering his offer. Unless she was going to ask him about her mother, she had no right to see him at all.

And could she do that over dinner?

Why not?

'How about if I picked you up about six-thirty?' he said casually, evidently expecting her to agree.

'Um—six-thirty.' Rachel licked her lips, mentally assessing her wardrobe. 'Well, all right.' She paused. 'I'll meet you downstairs.'

Matt gave a soft laugh. 'Don't you trust me to come up?'

Actually, it was herself she didn't trust, but she wasn't going to tell him that. 'I'll see you later, then,' she said, and, without giving him another chance to disconcert her, she put down the receiver.

With at least two hours to spare, Rachel took a leisurely shower. She washed her hair, too, and tried to give it some shape with the hand-drier the hotel provided. But without the right tools it wouldn't do what she wanted. So, giving up, she coiled it into a knot on top of her head.

What to wear was easier, because she'd only brought a limited number of garments with her. She hovered over skinny leggings, worn with a silky top, but decided the leggings might irritate her already hot legs.

She finally decided on a simple wrap dress of silk jersey. It was only thigh-length, and inclined to cling, but because it was black it wouldn't draw attention to her sunburn. A broad patent belt cinched her narrow waist, and she slipped matching heels onto her bare feet.

Her only concession to make-up had been the bronze shadow that coated her lids. And a similarly subtle lip gloss to give her mouth some colour. A handful of gold bangles around her wrist, and the amethyst pendant and earrings her parents had given her on her eighteenth birthday, and she was ready.

She looked smart, she thought, but not over-dressed. All the same, she hoped they weren't eating in the restaurant downstairs. She would hate to have another run-in with Mark Douglas.

When she went downstairs at precisely half-past-six Matt was waiting in the lobby. She'd half expected him to be wearing a suit, as he had the evening before, but his pleated khaki pants and cream linen shirt were definitely informal.

He looked every bit as attractive as he'd done earlier, moving with a lithe, cat-like grace to meet her at the foot of the stairs. His shirt was unbuttoned at his throat, and the khakis shaped his narrow hips and the powerful length of his legs.

She'd never known such a disturbing man, or one who wore his sexuality so easily. She was always aware of it, always aware of him. Yet, despite what had happened the night before—or maybe because of it—she was still so unsure of herself with him.

'A punctual woman,' he remarked drily. 'How unusual is that?'

'I'm always punctual,' replied Rachel primly, refusing to admit that she'd been ready and waiting for the past fifteen minutes. 'Are we dining in the hotel?'

'As you did last night, you mean?'

Matt's green eyes mocked her determination not to think of the way he'd seen her the night before. Naked, body splayed, one leg raised so he could bestow a lingering kiss behind her knee.

She felt a quiver of anticipation run over her. Oh, God, he'd been sucking on her nipple, his hand cupping her bottom. There was no way she could put that image out of her mind.

In an effort to distract herself, she said, 'I wanted to thank you again for what you said to Mark Douglas. I was dreading seeing him again.'

'Yeah, I know,' said Matt, reaching for one of her hands and tugging her gently towards the exit. 'If he troubles you again, just let me know.'

As if she could do that!

Rachel shook her head, but she didn't say the obvious. She didn't know where to reach him, except through the hotel. And she could imagine the speculation there would be if she asked one of the receptionists for his address.

And there was still her mother…

Somehow she had to find a way to ask him about his association with Sara Clairborne. Why, if they were only friends, hadn't her mother told her father what she was going to do? And the claim Sara had made about staying on the island. She couldn't have done that without some support from Matt.

Rachel's mind was buzzing, and it was almost a relief when Matt directed her to his Jeep. Obviously, wherever they were dining, it wasn't within walking distance.

It was almost completely dark, and the night was filled with the sound of cicadas. The atmosphere was warm and slightly humid, the air velvet-soft against her heated skin.

Matt helped her into the front of the Jeep and then walked round to get in beside her. His arm brushed hers as he settled in his seat, and her mouth went dry. She couldn't help it. Her eyes were drawn to the taut thigh only inches away across the console, the unmistakable bulge of muscle between his legs.

She so wanted to touch him. Every nerve in her body was on high alert, responding to his sensual appeal. The goosebumps that ran down her arms and legs were a silent acknowledgement of the effect he had upon her. She'd never experienced such an awareness of her own body, this shameless desire to give herself to him.

She sucked in a breath and he glanced curiously towards her. 'Are you all right?' he asked, and she wondered what he'd say if she told him exactly what she was thinking.

But, 'Fine,' she managed, her voice a little higher than it should be. 'Um—' She cleared her throat, trying to get control of her emotions. 'Where are we going? Is it far?'

'Not too far,' said Matt, which was hardly an answer.

She didn't know the island, so she had no idea what 'not too far' might mean. She tried to remember if they'd passed any restaurants that morning when he'd taken her to Mango Cove. But if they had she'd been too absorbed in other things to notice them.

When they left the small town behind, the road ahead of them seemed awfully dark. Rachel was used to driving in England, where even on the darkest roads there were houses or pubs, small villages. All she could see at present were tall hedges, or the startled eyes of the occasional small rodent attracted by the headlights of the Jeep.

As her eyes adjusted to the darkness, however, she glimpsed the ground falling away at the side of the road. And, because she was nervous, she found herself saying, 'Couldn't we have gone to Juno's again? I liked it there.'

'Did you?' Matt didn't sound as if he believed her. 'And, yes, we could have gone to Juno's, but I thought you might like to see Jaracoba.'

'Jaracoba?' Rachel's mind went blank. Was that the name of a place, or what?

'It's my father's house,' said Matt, glancing her way. 'As a matter of fact, he invited you to dinner.'

CHAPTER TEN

'OH!'

Rachel couldn't hide her disappointment. She'd thought Matt had invited her to have dinner with him, but now it seemed she'd been mistaken.

Yet wasn't this what she wanted? she argued with herself. An opportunity, perhaps, to confront him with her mother's reasons for being here?

'Don't get me wrong,' Matt continued, evidently sensing her ambivalence. 'It was at my instigation. Though I have to say my father wanted to meet you, too.'

'Why?'

The darkness gave Rachel the courage to be forthright. She doubted she'd have been so brave if Matt had been able to see her face.

'What do you want me to say?' Matt shrugged, glancing her way again, and, remembering the terrain, Rachel wished he'd keep his eyes on the road. 'Because you're Sara's daughter, I guess. He's known your mother for a lot of years.'

'He's known my mother...?' Rachel's breathing was suddenly suspended. 'Is—is your father's name Matthew Brody, too?' she asked, hoping against hope that this was the explanation for her mother's flight.

'No. Jacob,' said Matt, instantly killing that suspicion. He turned between tall gateposts. 'Welcome to Jaracoba.

My great-grandfather founded this plantation over a hundred years ago.'

But Rachel was so tense she hardly heard what he was saying. Her mind was focussed on the evening to come, and she dreaded the possibility that her mother might be here. She didn't want to see her with Matt, whatever their relationship. She was going to speak to him, she reminded herself. Just not like this.

The rasping sound of the tree frogs added to the chorus of the insects. There were fireflies buzzing amongst the trees, like tiny winking lights. But even the glorious scent of frangipani and night-blooming jasmine couldn't distract her. Why had Matt brought her here when he must know she wouldn't be welcome?

The house, when they reached it, briefly diverted her. It reminded her of pictures she'd seen of plantation houses in the southern United States. Painted white, with dark brown shutters and a wraparound porch, it was very impressive. Floodlights illuminated the front of the building and drew attention to the vine-draped balcony and the stately grace of its pillared façade.

Rachel lifted her hands and pressed her fingers to her lips as she gazed at the building. She'd guessed Matt's home would be beautiful, but she hadn't expected anything quite so magnificent as this.

'Do you like it?' Matt asked, turning off the Jeep's engine but making no attempt to get out of the vehicle. He ran the backs of his knuckles down her cheek, and she stiffened instinctively. 'Don't be so apprehensive. Pa's not a frightening man.'

Rachel swallowed. 'You should have told me where we were going.'

'Why?' Matt's dark brows arched. 'Would you have refused to come?'

Would she?

Her tongue circled her lips, unknowingly provocative. 'Will—will my mother be here?'

'No.' Matt spoke without hesitation.

Then, lifting his hand again, he probed her lips with his thumb. And Rachel couldn't stop herself. She bit down on the sensitive pad.

'Ow,' he howled, half humorously. Then, his eyes darkening, 'Promise to do that again later, when we're alone.'

'Will we be alone later?' Rachel couldn't prevent the question.

'Depend on it,' said Matt, his voice thickening, and before she could anticipate what he planned to do he'd pressed a hard kiss to her mouth.

'Good evenin'.'

The deep voice made Rachel jump. She'd been staring at Matt, bemused by the raw possession in his mouth, and it was an effort to turn her head and face the elderly West Indian man who was standing beside her door.

'Sorry to disturb you, Mr Matt,' he said, with some irony in his voice. 'But Mr Jacob, he heard you arrive and he's gettin' impatient, yeah?'

'Yeah, yeah.'

It was with an obvious effort that Matt pushed open his door and thrust his long legs out of the Jeep. Meanwhile, the man opened Rachel's door and said, 'Welcome to Jaracoba, Ms Claiborne.'

Rachel managed a smile. 'Thank you.' She allowed the man to assist her to alight. 'I'm—happy to be here.'

'Aren't you, though?' Matt was at her side now, his hand possessing her arm with undisguised ownership. His eyes mimicked her courtesy. 'This is Caleb, by the way. He's been here since my grandfather's time. Isn't that right, Caleb?'

'Surely is,' Caleb responded good-humouredly. 'Your father and Ms Diana are in the sitting room. Maggie'll be serving dinner in about fifteen minutes. That okay?'

'Whatever you say,' said Matt, guiding Rachel towards the flight of steps that led up to the porch. 'I guess we'll have time to get a drink.'

Despite her awareness of the strong fingers wrapped around her arm, Rachel couldn't help admiring the beauty of the old building. There were dark bamboo chairs and benches on the porch, each upholstered in a pretty navy and white striped pattern. There were planters filled with climbing plants and pots spilling fragrant shrubs across the polished boards of the floor.

Rachel guessed it would be an ideal place to sit on a hot day, but before she had a chance to take it all in Matt was leading her through a cool tiled hall and into a formal dining room.

She saw a table that could easily seat a dozen guests, gleaming with silver and crystal. Curls of ivory napery were set on bone-white plates, and a centrepiece that combined a silver candelabra and scarlet hibiscus was the perfect complement.

By the time Matt opened the door into the adjoining sitting room Rachel was feeling dazed and definitely apprehensive. Surely anyone who lived in these surroundings had to be intimidating, and it was doubly disturbing when she felt she was here under false pretences.

There were three people in the huge sitting room. One, she saw at once, was Matt's sister Amalie, and the two older people were obviously his parents.

Despite the effort it evidently cost him, Jacob Brody got instantly to his feet. Leaning heavily on his walking stick, he would have started towards them if Matt hadn't stopped him.

'Hey, it's okay,' he said, leaving Rachel's side to go and help the older man back into his chair. 'Rachel will forgive you. Won't you, Rachel?'

Rachel made a helpless gesture. 'I—of course,' she said

quickly, and was aware of the older woman getting to her feet also, and coming towards her.

'You must forgive Jacob, Rachel,' she said. 'He forgets he's not as agile as he used to be.' She smiled. 'I'm Diana, by the way. And that—' she indicated the girl still lounging on a huge red velvet sofa '—as I'm sure you know, is Amalie.'

'Yes.' Rachel allowed Diana to shake her hand in welcome. 'We—er—we met in town the other day.'

'So I believe.' Diana's tone was dry, and Rachel wondered what Amalie had told her mother about their encounter. 'Let me get you a drink.'

'I'll do that,' said Matt at once, reaching out a hand to beckon Rachel to join him. 'Come and meet my old man, Rachel. He can't wait to introduce himself.'

'Not so much of the old,' retorted Jacob Brody staunchly, his handshake unexpectedly firm. 'Take no notice of my son, Rachel. I admit I did want to meet you. Are you enjoying your stay on St Antoine?'

'Very much,' said Rachel, and at Jacob's suggestion she took the chair nearest to his. 'It's a beautiful island.'

'That is is,' agreed Jacob, with obvious satisfaction. 'Our family have lived here for almost two hundred years. Not always in such comfort, naturally.' He smiled and looked up at his son. 'Did you say something about getting Rachel a drink?'

'Yeah, I did, didn't I?' Matt's smile was rueful. 'What can I get you, Rachel? A glass of wine? Or perhaps you'd like a cocktail like Diana and Amalie are having.'

Diana?

Rachel frowned as she looked up at him, and she could tell by his lazily amused expression that he understood her confusion 'Um—white wine, I think,' she said, aware she was being overly cautious. But, heavens, did he call his mother *Diana*? Or had she been misled? Wasn't Diana his mother, after all?

'Sure?'

His eyes were mocking her again, but she refused to be diverted. 'Yes, please,' she said firmly. 'Thank you.'

'So go and do your duty, Matt!' exclaimed his father impatiently, and Matt's mouth compressed in an effort to control his mirth.

'Oh, I intend to,' he said, his eyes on Rachel as he spoke, and she felt the hot colour rising up her throat. 'Excuse me for a moment, won't you?'

Despite herself, Rachel couldn't help watching him as he crossed the room to where a drinks cart had been installed. He took a bottle of white wine and another of beer from the chilled compartment, filling a glass for Rachel that seemed inordinately large.

'Have you seen much of the island?'

Jacob was speaking again, and Rachel forced her attention back to the man beside her. 'A little,' she said, biting her lower lip before continuing, 'I joined one of those picnic cruises this morning, and that was—that was—'

'Interesting?' suggested Matt, appearing beside her. He handed her the glass of wine, his amusement evident again. 'Unfortunately it didn't work out quite as well as she'd intended. She had to contend with—um—sunburn. Isn't that right, Rachel?'

Rachel's face was burning now. 'That's right,' she said tightly, knowing that Matt knew full well what she'd thought he'd been about to say. She straightened her spine as Matt propped his hip on the arm of her chair instead of seeking another. 'But yesterday your son was kind enough to—um—lend me some cream his grandmother used to use.'

Matt grinned, apparently enjoying her attempt to turn the tables. 'I think it's done some good. Don't you, Diana?'

Diana, who had returned to her seat beside her daughter on the sofa, nodded thoughtfully. 'Charley certainly knew a thing or two about herbal medicine,' she agreed. 'That's Grandma

Charlotte,' she explained for Rachel's benefit. 'I've used the cream myself on many occasions.'

Rachel smiled, trying to behave as if Matt's thigh wasn't wedged against her shoulder. He was holding his bottle of beer in one hand, but the other was hovering somewhere near the nape of her neck. Just occasionally a finger brushed her skin and she shivered. And, while her brain was warning her not to play his game, the temptation to reach up and cover his hand with hers was almost overwhelming.

She managed to resist, however, and thankfully the conversation became more general. Jacob wanted to know if Matt had had enquiries for any more charters, and Amalie grumbled that they weren't supposed to talk business when they had a guest.

Diana asked about her job in England. She seemed genuinely interested when Rachel explained she worked for a small local newspaper in Chingford.

'Jacob writes, too,' she said, drawing an impatient disclaimer from Matt's father. 'He does,' she insisted. 'He's researching a history of the island and the Brodys' part in it.' She chuckled. 'I've warned him he'll probably find out his ancestors were pirates or some such. No one on these islands can be absolutely sure their family wasn't involved in that or the slave trade.'

Rachel smiled. She liked Diana. The woman was doing her best to make her feel at home. Amalie, meanwhile, just sipped her cocktail, only making the most unenthusiastic attempt to air her views.

'Well, I think it's exciting,' Rachel said. 'My job just involves getting in touch with local businesses and asking them if they'd like to advertise in the paper. I've always envied people who have the talent to write.'

'That's a matter of opinion,' said Jacob drily, 'I'd much prefer to be out and about on my own again.'

'Oh, Jacob…'

Diana spoke sympathetically, and while his father was otherwise engaged Matt bent and put his lips close to Rachel's ear.

She sucked in a breath, aware of Amalie watching them and not sure what he was planning to do, but he only said softly, 'Pa had a stroke about three months ago. He's recovering well, but the doctors have warned him he can't go on doing as much as he did before.'

'Oh!'

Rachel pressed her fingers to her lips, her uneven breathing giving her away. Matt straightened, his eyes revealing he'd known exactly what she was thinking.

Trying to concentrate on other matters, Rachel acknowledged that, despite his evident weakness, Matt's father wasn't an old man. Evidently the stroke accounted for his use of a walking stick. But in spite of a small stoop he was still tall, like his son, and it must gall him to be confined to the house, however beautiful his surroundings.

'He'll be okay,' Matt added, as Diana turned back to address her daughter.

'Amalie, why don't you ask Rachel if she'd like another glass of wine?'

'Oh, no. Thank you.' Rachel spread her fingers over the rim of the glass that was still more than half full. 'I'm not much of a drinker, I'm afraid.'

'Everything in moderation,' murmured Matt teasingly, and Amalie gave her a sulky look.

'You should relax a little, Rachel,' she said, draining the dregs of her cocktail with a careless flourish. 'And don't let my brother fool you. He's not half as innocent as he seems.'

'Amalie!'

It was her father who spoke now, and the girl had the grace to colour slightly. 'Well,' she said defensively. 'We all know why he had to invite her here.'

'I invited her,' said Jacob coldly. 'And if you can't keep a civil tongue in your head, young lady, you can spend the rest of the evening in your room.'

A sudden tap on the door was never more welcome, as far as Rachel was concerned. She had felt Matt tense beside her, and knew it was only a matter of time before he entered the exchange.

But Caleb's appearance diverted all of them. 'Dinner's ready when you are, Mr Jacob,' he said politely, and Matt's father pushed himself determinedly to his feet.

'Not a moment too soon,' he said, giving his daughter a final warning glance. He held out a hand to Rachel. 'Will you give me your arm, my dear?'

'Of course.'

With a nervous look in Matt's direction, Rachel joined his father for the procession into the dining room. And she saw at once something she hadn't noticed earlier: only one end of the impressive table had been laid for dinner.

With Matt's assistance, Jacob was seated at the head of the table, with Diana and Rachel on one side and Matt and Amalie on the other. Rachel found herself talking mainly to Diana, the width of the table precluding any private conversation with Matt.

The meal was delicious, but Rachel ate very little. A lobster soufflé that melted in the mouth was followed by freshly caught grouper, a fish Rachel had never tasted before. Then the tenderest of fillet steaks with 'rice and peas', which was really rice and red kidney beans, and a mix of exotic vegetables.

By the time dessert came around Rachel had to refuse. Although she'd only picked at her food, she knew she couldn't eat another thing. She was sure the passionfruit mousse was delectable, as Diana said, but all she wanted was coffee to finish the meal.

She noticed Matt hadn't shown much of an appetite either. He spoke often with his father, and she guessed they were talking business again. She encountered Amalie's eyes a time or two, quite by accident on her part, though probably not so on the girl's. That comment about Matt not being as innocent as he appeared still stuck in her mind.

'It's the only chance Jacob gets to find out what's going on in his absence,' murmured Diana in a low voice. 'He knows Matt is perfectly capable of running the company, but I'm afraid my husband is something of a work junkie.'

So Diana *was* Jacob's wife. 'Have you been married long?'

'Heavens, yes.' Diana spoke reminiscently. 'It's going to be thirty-five years in July. I can hardly believe it.' She grimaced. 'That's probably why Jacob used to spend so much time out of the house.'

Rachel smiled. 'My father's like that,' she said, feeling a renewed sense of guilt that she hadn't kept Ralph Claiborne informed of what she'd discovered. 'He enjoys his work, too.'

'What does he do?' asked Diana politely.

'Oh, he's an accountant,' replied Rachel, aware that Matt was also listening to their exchange. 'He was going to retire last year, but he changed his mind.' She paused then, and met Matt's considering gaze with one of her own. 'I think he wishes he had now.'

'Really? Why?'

Diana was interested, but Rachel was wishing she hadn't mentioned her father at all.

'Oh—just events,' she said offhandedly, accepting another cup of coffee from the maid who'd served their dinner. 'Thank you. This is delicious.'

'It's our own blend, you know.' To her relief, Jacob had heard what she'd said and now chose to enter their conversation. 'We cultivate it here at Jaracoba. Not an enormous amount, you understand, but enough for our own needs and the needs of most of the islanders.'

'Well, it's certainly good,' said Rachel admiringly. 'I'm ashamed to say I usually use instant at home.'

'Do you live with your parents?' asked Diana, and Rachel shook her head.

'No. I have a small apartment of my own.'

'Of your own?' Matt took her up on it. 'No partner?'

'No partner,' she said firmly, aware that she was blushing again. But, heavens, did he think she'd have allowed him to—well—touch her, if she'd been involved with someone else?

But perhaps he wasn't so discriminating...

The sound of a car racing up the drive carried on the still night air. An engine was revving far too noisily, tyres squealing, brakes screaming, as the vehicle was brought to a halt.

'What the devil—?' began Jacob irritably, half rising to his feet and then sinking back again when the door half opened and Caleb inserted his head into the space he'd created.

'You've got a visitor,' he was beginning, somewhat nervously, when the door was thrust open. Sara Claiborne, was just behind him, glaring over his shoulder, her eyes accusing as they swept round the table.

Rachel wanted to die. She felt sure her mother must have followed her here. Had she gone to the hotel and discovered her daughter had left with Matt Brody? Might they even have told her he was taking her to his home?

Whatever, surely Sara hadn't gone to the hotel dressed like that? Her scarlet catsuit clung to her generous curves; her stiletto heels were digging into the carpet.

She looked like a caricature of the woman Rachel had known all her life, and she couldn't understand what was going on.

'What do you want, Sara?'

It was Matt who spoke, pushing back his chair and regarding the visitor with a guarded gaze.

And Rachel realised she'd been wrong. Her mother hadn't come here to find her. It was Matt she wanted to see. Matt who, in spite of his obvious reluctance, brought a possessive smile to her face.

But then, as if remembering, her eyes moved back to Rachel again.

'What's *she* doing here?' she demanded, as if she had the right to do so. But now Jacob had had enough.

'I invited her,' he said. 'This is my home, and I'll invite who I like. I suggest you stop embarrassing yourself and Matt, Sara, and go back to Mango Key.'

CHAPTER ELEVEN

MATT drove Rachel back some thirty minutes later.

He was silent on the journey, and she couldn't exactly blame him. It must have been embarrassing, having the two women he was involved with in the room together. It had been embarrassing for her, goodness knew. And she'd done nothing wrong.

Yet.

But she refused to think about almost making love with Matt the evening before. She had to pretend that it had never happened. And, let's face it, she reminded herself, nothing *had* happened.

Yet.

She shook her head, as if by doing so she could shake such thoughts away. But it wasn't easy. She was remembering that despite Jacob's words Sara hadn't agreed to leave until she'd had a private conversation with Matt. He'd escorted her out to her car, and in his absence conversation had stalled. Sara's arrival had disturbed all of them, and only Amalie had seemed to be enjoying the situation.

The return journey seemed to be over far too quickly. In spite of what had happened Rachel was sorry the evening had had to end like this. She'd been so full of anticipation at its start. But perhaps this was payback for thinking of no one but herself.

For once, Matt turned into the hotel forecourt. And instead

of dropping her off at the entrance, as she'd expected, he parked the vehicle and got out. He'd circled the car and pulled open her door, too, before she'd had time to anticipate his actions. Then, helping her out, he said flatly, 'We need to talk.'

In spite of what she'd been thinking, Rachel knew that wasn't going to happen. Not tonight, anyway. Not while she was still distressed over what her mother had said.

'I—don't think so,' she said, turning towards the hotel entrance, but Matt's hand gripped her biceps.

'I do,' he said grimly. 'Come on. We'll go up to my suite.'

'Your suite?'

Rachel turned shocked eyes in his direction, and Matt gave her a weary look. 'You think I don't keep a suite of rooms at the hotel, just in case I need them?' he enquired drily. 'Sometimes it's not convenient to drive back to my house.'

Rachel shook her head. 'Even so...'

'Even so, nothing,' he said, turning her towards the entrance again. 'Come on. I'll buy you a drink before we go upstairs.'

'I—I don't want a drink,' stammered Rachel, even though the kick of alcohol might have been exactly what she needed.

'Not downstairs?' Matt chose to misunderstand her. 'Okay. I'll get one of the staff to bring a bottle to my rooms.'

'You don't understand—'

'No. *You* don't understand,' Matt interrupted her shortly, as they crossed the lobby. 'Wait here. I'll just speak to the barman about a bottle of wine.'

Rachel was almost to the top of the stairs when he caught up with her. She'd tried to hurry, but in her high heels it hadn't been easy. Matt was able to vault up two stairs at a time, and she had to concede there was no way she could get away from him in the hotel anyway.

When she would have turned towards her room, however, he stopped her. 'It's this way,' he said, and to her amazement, he directed her towards the double panelled doors which she knew led into the office. Of course the office would be empty at this time of day, but all the same...

Deciding she could hardly question his decision without provoking his curiosity, she shook herself free of his hand and walked beside him along the gallery. She realised they were in full view of anyone looking up from the foyer below, but she resigned herself to the knowledge that that was par for the course.

As expected, the office was deserted. Only dim security lighting illuminated desks and filing cabinets, the fax and printing machines she'd seen a few days ago. Surely Matt didn't intend that they should have a conversation here? He had mentioned a suite of rooms.

Matt closed the door behind them and then led the way across the room to where another door gave access to a narrow corridor. He switched on overhead lights and motioned for her to follow him. He then opened a door a few yards further on, and indicated that she should precede him into the room.

A switch at the door caused several lamps to spring to life, and Rachel saw at once that it was a small sitting room. Well, small by Jaracoba standards, she thought, her mind still filled with the magnificent dimensions of his home.

Twin leather sofas faced one another across a gleaming occasional table, their black surfaces highlighted by cushions in red and gold. There was a sound system and a large television; undrawn curtains hung at three long windows, matching the cushions in design.

Rachel was surprised by the beauty of the room. It was such an unexpected find beyond the commercial environs of the office. There were other doors that evidently gave access to a bathroom and a bedroom. Maybe even a kitchen, although she doubted Matt would bother making meals here.

Matt closed the door behind them and then leaned back against it. 'Sit down,' he said. 'The wine will arrive shortly.'

'I don't mind standing,' Rachel said, wandering across to the windows. But there was little to see beyond the panes but the floodlit grounds of the hotel.

Matt shrugged, and moments later there was a tentative knock at the door. He swung it open, then took the tray from the waiter with little ceremony, closing the door in the man's face with what Rachel recognised as barely controlled impatience.

It was only as he set the tray on the low table that she saw he'd ordered champagne. A bottle of Krug sat beside two crystal glasses, and, although she knew little about such things, she guessed only the best would do for him.

When he straightened again, and looked directly at her, Rachel shifted uneasily. His eyes were dark with anger and there was little compassion in his gaze.

'Come and sit down,' he said, and this time it sounded like an order. 'I have no intention of discussing anything with you hovering over there like Marley's ghost.'

Rachel squared her shoulders. 'Do we have anything to discuss?'

Matt's mouth twisted, and she saw the pulse beating at his temple. Oh, he was angry all right, she thought apprehensively. No wonder she was feeling so alarmed.

He blew out a breath, and for a moment she wondered if he intended to force her to obey him. But she should have known better. Instead, he bent and lifted the champagne, expertly easing out the cork and pouring himself a glass.

She was sure he drank it without tasting it. Which seemed his intention. He poured himself another and then looked at her again. 'You know,' he said, 'I can stay here all night if necessary.'

Rachel sighed. She was half wishing now that she'd not created this stand-off. He was right. It was silly. And counter-productive.

'All right,' she said, and with a little shrug she stepped

nervously towards him. 'I know you can always out-do me when it comes to an argument.' She paused beside one of the sofas, her nails digging into the soft leather. 'What did you want to talk about?'

Matt closed his eyes for a moment, as if he didn't quite believe her. Then, opening them again, he swallowed half the liquid in his glass before setting it back on the tray.

'Sit down,' he said, pointing to the sofa opposite him. 'Or do you want me to think you're scared of me? Believe me, you should be.'

Rachel remained where she was. 'Why don't you just tell me why you've brought me here?' she demanded. 'I assume you're feeling peeved about what happened. Well, don't think you can take your frustration out on me...'

'My frustration? My *frustration*?' The oath he uttered didn't bear repeating. 'You don't know anything about my frustration! If you did, you wouldn't stand there baiting me with stupid complaints.'

'You don't think I have room to complain?' she exclaimed, using anger to mask her apprehension. 'How do you think I felt when my mother walked into the room tonight?'

'How do I think *you* felt?' Matt was incredulous. 'How do you think *I* felt? My father can do without that kind of stress in his present condition.'

Rachel shook her head. 'I didn't invite her.'

Matt swore again. 'Do you think I did?'

'I don't know, do I?' she mumbled. 'Are you having an affair with her?'

'God, no.' He sounded appalled.

'But she came here to see you.'

Matt sighed then. 'That doesn't mean I'm having an affair with her, Rachel. Our relationship is nothing like that.'

Rachel wanted to ask what it *was* like, but she felt she'd gone as far as she could tonight. 'Anyway,' she said. 'It doesn't matter now. I'm tired. I want to go to bed.'

Matt stared at her, his green eyes as dark as laurel. His look was intent, dangerous, and despite everything Rachel couldn't look away.

'I want to go to bed, too,' he said, and now he moved, closing the space between them. His warm breath fanned her cheek and his quickened breathing matched her own.

Rachel would have backed away again, but his hand at her nape prevented her from moving at all.

'I want to go to bed with you,' he added, bending to brush the corner of her mouth with his lips. 'I want to make love with you and sleep with you and then make love with you again.'

Rachel's breath caught in the back of her throat. This was so much more than she had expected. He was so close she could feel the heat of his body enveloping her; so close she was suddenly aware of the pulse beating at the centre of her core.

Warm wet fluid drenched her panties and her limbs went totally weak. 'Matt—'

She tried to make a protest, but the truth was she didn't really want to stop him. She'd never felt a need like this before, never experienced such a craving that yearned to be fulfilled.

He moved even closer, taking the evening bag she was holding like a barrier in front of her and tossing it aside. Then he slipped an arm about her waist and pulled her against him, her breasts crushed against his chest, her hips against the hard muscles of his thighs.

'Sweet,' he said, his voice thickening with emotion, pushing a thigh between her quivering legs. 'Do you have any idea how much I want you?'

Then his mouth was on hers, hard and passionate. His tongue plunged between her teeth, exploring the moist cavity he found within. His tongue caressed hers, mated with hers, causing her to lean against him. And she heard his growl of appreciation when she allowed him to suck her tongue into his mouth.

She couldn't fail to be aware of his arousal, and her hands sought the waistband of his khakis for support. His hand cupped her chin, angled her face to please him, lengthening and deepening his kiss.

His free hand slid over her scalp. She felt the knot she'd made of her hair unravel, felt the weight of it loose about her shoulders.

'So beautiful,' he said, allowing the silky strands to slide through his fingers. Then he lowered his head and buried his face in its soft folds.

Blood was thundering through Rachel's veins like liquid fire. The increasing pressure of his erection against her stomach made her feel weak. He brushed a strand of hair from her cheek, and looked down at her with undisguised hunger.

'I've wanted you since that morning at Mango Cove,' he said huskily. 'Tell me you don't want me, too, and I'll let you go.'

Rachel shook her head. 'I—I can't,' she admitted. Her breathing was becoming more and more shallow, and he tipped back her head and trailed hot kisses down her throat.

'That's what I thought,' he breathed with evident satisfaction, his possessive touch making her feel as if she might swoon with pleasure.

A hot wave of desire was surging over her, making her body tremble, sweeping all her inhibitions away. She hadn't known it was possible to feel so out of control, yet so aware of what she was doing. Her body seemed to be working on instinct, knowing automatically what he wanted her to do.

When his mouth returned to hers again, her lips parted instinctively. She discovered his shirt had pulled free of his pants at the back, and her palms spread sensuously over hot male flesh. She'd never touched a man in this way before, never wanted the ultimate pleasure of exploring a man's body.

But she remembered how Matt had looked that day at the beach, and she wanted to see him that way again.

She was hardly aware that Matt had found the cords that tied the wraparound jersey about her. It was only when she felt the cool, air-conditioned draught on her shoulders that she realised her dress was down around her waist. And only there because of the closeness of their bodies. If Matt stepped away, it would tumble to the floor.

She was diverted by Matt's mouth caressing the upper slopes of her breasts. Her bra was still in place, but she knew it revealed as much as it concealed. She glanced down and saw her breasts were swollen, the nipples straining hard against the flimsy lace.

Matt cupped her breasts in his hands, and then startled her by bending to suckle her through her bra. The fabric got wet, but it was so sensual, so intimate. It added another feverish dimension to her need.

Then Matt unhooked the bra and discarded it. 'Let's find somewhere more comfortable,' he said huskily, and picked her up in his arms.

Rachel's head felt as if it was spinning. It was all happening too fast and she was so not ready for it. Nevertheless, she wound her arms around his neck and pressed her face against his throat. Her cheek brushed against his chin, felt the roughness of his stubble. And the scent of his skin was so intoxicating that she forgot to be apprehensive.

Matt kicked open a door and she glimpsed the austerity of a dark carpet and the familiar dimensions of a huge bed. The light streaming in from the living room showed the silk spread that covered the bed. She felt its coolness against her bare back as Matt laid her on it. It reminded her that, although she was almost naked, Matt was still fully clothed.

An image she recalled from the previous evening.

She would have been happy to remain in semi-darkness, but Matt said, 'We need some light.' He turned on the lamp beside the bed and surveyed her with obvious satisfaction. 'I want to see you,' he said, peeling off his shirt with fingers that weren't quite steady. 'I want to see all of you.'

Rachel caught her breath when his hands went to his waistband. She wanted him naked, of course she did, but she couldn't help feeling nervous.

Then the bed depressed as Matt came to kneel beside her. 'You do it,' he said thickly, drawing her hands to the buckle of his belt.

Rachel took a gulp of air. She was trying to ground herself, but it wasn't working. Pushing herself into a sitting position, she prepared to do as he'd asked.

But her thighs parted automatically when she leaned forward, and Matt groaned and slipped his hand between her legs. He cupped her through her panties and his voice was hoarse with satisfaction when he said, 'You're wet.'

Rachel made a helpless gesture, not knowing how to react.

Matt had no such inhibitions. 'Incredible,' he continued, his finger invading the hem of her briefs and parting the tender lips of her womanhood. 'So ready,' he groaned, his voice rough with feeling as he found the already swollen nub at her core.

It was almost impossible to do anything while Matt was caressing her. The excitement building inside her was hastened by the erotic movements of his hand, and she wanted to part her legs wider, let him do whatever he wanted to prolong these amazing feelings. She gave a breathless little moan of anguish.

Somehow she managed to loosen his belt and unzip his khakis, though when his erection sprang into her hands she was understandably shaken. God, he was so big, she thought, her knowledge of a man's anatomy scanty at best. How could she want him so much and yet be so apprehensive?

Matt kicked off his shoes and his pants and then climbed

onto the bed beside her. He eased her back, and she relaxed again when he covered her mouth with his. Yet she couldn't stop herself from arching against him, from wanting more, much more, from him. Her hands sought him now, wanting to please him, and she was alarmed when he gave a muffled groan of protest.

'Easy,' he said against her mouth, nudging her thighs apart so he could lie between her legs. 'I'm only human,' he added ruefully. 'How much more of this do you think I can take?'

Rachel looked up at him, her eyes wide. 'A lot more, I hope,' she said impulsively, and then curled her legs around him when he buried his face between her breasts.

Once again she was conscious of the liquid pooling inside her. She could feel his erection pressing at the apex of her legs and she pressed herself against him, wanting him inside her. But instead he drew back, hooking his thumbs into the waistband of her panties and drawing them down her legs.

Then Matt was pressing his face against the damp curls he'd exposed. 'I—you can't do that!' she exclaimed, in a panic now. Her nails dug into his shoulders in protest at first, and then her hands sought his head, holding him closer.

'Better?' he asked, and all she could do was nod helplessly, lost in the needs he was inspiring.

Then his tongue probed between the curls and her body exploded. Waves and waves of pleasure tore through her, and despite her inexperience she knew what he'd done.

'But—I wanted *you*,' she whispered, and he trailed wet kisses across the slight mound of her stomach.

'And you'll have me,' he told her softly. 'I wanted to please you first.'

'You have,' she assured him as he worked his way up her body, nuzzling and kissing and biting her tender flesh. So much he'd rocked her whole world.

When he straddled her she tensed again, but only slightly. She was still experiencing the lingering rhythms of the pleasure he had given her, and even when he nudged her opening and eased a little way inside she wasn't alarmed.

'You're tight,' he said, but the way he said it she knew it wasn't a criticism. Then he cupped his hands beneath her bottom and lifted her to meet his urgent thrust.

He stifled the cry she uttered with his mouth, but he couldn't ignore the sudden obstruction that met his invasion. Yet he couldn't draw back. It was much too late for that. All he could do was bury himself inside her and then lift his head to stare down at her. The tears that had filled her eyes were a silent admission of what he'd done.

'Why didn't you tell me?' he demanded.

Rachel's tongue circled her lips. 'Does it matter?'

'Of course it matters,' he said. 'God, Rachel, you were a virgin. You should have told me.'

'I thought you wanted me,' she whispered.

'I did want you,' he retorted. 'God help me, I want you still. But it's wrong.'

'Is it wrong if I want you, too?' she protested. 'Please, Matt.' She felt his body stirring inside her and discovered she wanted more, needed more. 'Don't stop now.'

Matt gave a low groan that was half anguished, half humorous. 'I don't think I can stop,' he admitted harshly. 'But you've got to tell me if I hurt you again.'

Rachel nodded, slightly apprehensive again now, but she had no reason to be. Matt was so gentle at first, so controlled, that she felt her body relaxing until she felt his length filling her completely.

Then, as his own needs began to take over, her emotions quickened. He drew back, almost to the point of total withdrawal, before surging forward again. And as he did so her response became more demanding, and the feelings she'd had when Matt had seduced her with his tongue came back stronger than before.

There was no pain now. Her body was slick with moisture,

and Matt's movements created a wonderful friction that made what she'd felt before seem tame. This was real, this was urgent, this was making every nerve in her body react to his need. And the feelings just kept on building, until she felt as if all her senses had reached overload.

But then something magical happened. It was as if she'd been climbing a mountain and now she'd reached its highest pinnacle. With arms spread wide, she floated out over the precipice, her cry of fulfilment both mindless and sapped with pleasure…

CHAPTER TWELVE

MATT opened his eyes to find Rachel tiptoeing across the bedroom.

He must have fallen asleep, he realised, and with good reason. As well as making love a second time, which had been just as devastating as the first, they'd opened the champagne. He'd drunk several glasses of the intoxicating wine before exhaustion had obviously tugged him into oblivion.

But they had shared the most sensational sex he'd ever known. Somehow it had been more than just sex, he mused. It had been the closest thing to a spiritual experience he'd ever known. He'd never felt like this before. Never felt that instantaneous recognition of something stronger than himself.

'What are you doing?' he demanded now, propping himself up on his elbows. It was still dark outside, but there was a faint glow of sunrise on the horizon. The lamp beside the bed was still burning, however, and by its light he could see that Rachel had already found her panties and put them on.

'It's nearly morning,' Rachel whispered, and he noticed she had her arms crossed over her bosom.

He felt slightly irritated. Dammit, it wasn't as if he hadn't seen her breasts before. Seen them and kissed them and suckled from them, he remembered, his body stirring in spite of himself. God, he still wanted her. He had the uneasy feeling he was never going to have enough of her.

'It's still early,' he said, trying to keep his tone even. When what he really wanted to do was bound out of bed and carry her back into his lair. 'Come back to bed.'

'I don't want to be here when—when whoever occupies that office out there turns up for work,' Rachel declared, ignoring his suggestion. 'I'm sorry if I disturbed you. I didn't intend to.'

'So—what?' Matt stared at her, his mouth slightly belligerent. 'You were going to sneak out of here and hope I didn't hear you go?'

'It's not sneaking,' Rachel protested.

'What would you call it, then?' Matt scowled. 'Don't tell me you're regretting what happened last night?'

'Heavens, no.' Her response was so spontaneous he couldn't help but believe her. 'It's just—well—I can see you later, I suppose. After—after I've had a shower and dressed in some different clothes.'

'You could have a shower here.' Matt gestured towards the adjoining bathroom.

'No, thank you.' Rachel turned towards the door. 'I'll just go and find the rest of my things.'

'Let me,' said Matt, thrusting back the covers and getting out of bed. He wanted her to see his nakedness, to show he wasn't ashamed of himself, or her.

Rachel caught her breath at the sight of him. But at least it made her forget about covering herself as she opened the bedroom door.

Then he was behind her, drawing her back against his already aroused body. His shaft pulsed against her bottom, and she sucked in a little breath as his hands slid round to cover her breasts.

'Let me,' he said, bending his head to nibble on her shoulder. 'Don't go,' he added huskily. 'I want to make love with you again.'

Another indrawn breath proved she wasn't immune to his caresses. He felt her press herself against him almost involuntarily, and the feel of her soft bottom cradling his erection brought him close to losing control.

But, 'I'd better go,' she insisted, despite all reactions to the contrary. 'I mean it, Matt. I promise I'll see you later. I just need a little time to—to freshen up.'

He had to let her go. He had to watch as she picked up her bra and stuffed it into her handbag. Then she pulled on the wraparound gown she'd been wearing and hurriedly tied the cords. Without her bra, the dress was undeniably provocative, and with a muffled exclamation Matt said, 'Wait!'

This time she did wait, probably because she didn't want to spark his anger. There'd been sufficient irritation in his voice for her to realise he meant what he said. In a matter of minutes he'd hauled on his pants and thrown his shirt over his shoulders. 'I'll take you back to your room,' he said. 'We don't want anyone getting the wrong idea.'

He thought she wanted to argue, but perhaps she remembered Mark Douglas and changed her mind. 'Thank you,' she said, and, looking at her, he wondered if she really didn't regret what had happened.

She seemed so fragile, so remote; so much the innocent. He couldn't help but blame himself for taking advantage of her.

Rachel spent some time in the shower. It was good to feel the water sluicing all the perspiration from her skin. She felt tired—and a little sore—but otherwise wonderfully happy. It had been the most amazing night of her life and she couldn't wait to see Matt again.

She hadn't wanted to leave him that morning. She knew he had been concerned about her, and it would have been so easy to abandon any worries about what other people might think and crawl back into bed.

Into Matt's bed, she reminded herself with a little shiver

of excitement. Would he expect to sleep with her tonight? She really hoped so.

But then she remembered her mother.

She still had no doubt that Sara Claiborne had come to Jaracoba looking for Matt. He'd virtually admitted as much. But he'd also denied that he was having an affair with her.

So what did that mean? Had they had an affair in the past? Had her mother come here hoping to resurrect their relationship?

It was a situation Rachel didn't even want to consider, but she had to. Her father was in England, waiting for her to get back to him with some good news. But what could she tell him? That her mother had changed? That she was seriously thinking of staying on the island? That, whatever Matt said, Sara's association with him was anything but over?

She examined herself in the mirror when she came out of the shower cubicle. She didn't think she'd changed, outwardly at least. But she knew she was different inside. It wasn't so much a physical thing, although she knew that had changed too. But psychologically she was a different person.

There was another bite mark on her shoulder and she ran her fingers over it. And felt a tingling sensation right down to her toes. Her mouth was slightly swollen, but she wasn't really surprised. Matt's kisses had been full of raw passion.

However crazy she was, she couldn't wait to see him again. If she'd known the extension number of his apartment she might have called him. So it was probably just as well that she didn't. They had to talk again before anything more significant happened between them.

Although what could be more significant than last night's lovemaking?

Shaking her head, she grabbed a towel from the rack and quickly dried herself. Her hair was still damp when she fastened it back with a scrunchie, but she was too impatient to spend much time on it. Besides, her hands weren't quite steady, and she knew that whatever she did it would still persist in curling about her temples and her nape.

She dressed in lime-green shorts and a scoop-necked tee shirt which successfully hid the bite on her shoulder. She could do nothing about the mark on her neck, but the heat in her skin had faded and her incipient tan made it less conspicuous.

She used her mascara brush and an amber-coloured lip-gloss, slipped canvas flats onto her feet, and, after collecting her bag, left her room.

Her eyes were instinctively drawn to the double doors that led to both the office and Matt's apartment. But there was no sign of the hotel's owner, and, despite a sense of disappointment, Rachel descended the stairs.

Deciding that if Matt did come looking for her he would expect her to be on the patio, having breakfast, she crossed the foyer to the restaurant. A waiter seated her overlooking the pool, and she ordered coffee and French toast. For practically the first time since she'd come St Antoine she was hungry, and her lips twitched in rueful amusement. That was one outcome of losing her virginity that she hadn't anticipated.

She was just finishing her third cup of coffee when a flurry of movement caught her eye. She'd enjoyed the French toast, served with maple syrup, and despite a lingering sense of apprehension she was feeling pleasantly replete.

But the movement, accompanied by an impatient exchange with the waiter, drew her attention to the woman who was crossing the patio towards her.

Her mother.

Rachel caught her breath. She couldn't help it. She so didn't want to have a conversation with her mother. Not until she'd spoken to Matt again, anyway.

But that wasn't to be, and, putting down her cup, she got automatically to her feet. 'Hi, Mum.'

'I've told you not to call me Mum!' exclaimed Sara Claiborne angrily. Then, turning back to the waiter who had followed her, she added, 'Just fetch another pot of coffee. I don't want anything to eat.'

'Yes, ma'am.'

The waiter looked to Rachel, as if seeking her approval, and she nodded. What else could she do? This was her mother, after all. However outrageous she looked, still in the tight-fitting catsuit she'd worn the night before. Had she been to bed? Rachel didn't think so. And she suddenly wished she'd never had such a rich breakfast.

Sara pulled out a chair and sat down opposite her daughter. 'You're still here, then,' she said flatly. 'I thought I asked you to go back to London.'

Rachel sighed. 'You knew I was still here, Mum. You saw me at Matt's house last night.'

'I saw you at his *father's* house last night,' her mother corrected her. 'Matt doesn't live with his father. He has his own house. Where do you think I've been staying?'

'I see.'

It was a low blow, and Rachel did her best to hide her reaction.

'Oh, yes.' Sara knew her too well to be deceived by Rachel's attempt at indifference. 'It's a beautiful house. It overlooks the ocean. I'm very happy there.'

Rachel was sure she was. She just wished Matt had told her where her mother was staying. But then until last night they hadn't spoken about her mother at all.

'What do you want, Mum,' she asked now. 'Why have you come here?'

Sara gave her an incredulous look. 'What do I *want*?' she echoed. 'You know what I want, Rachel. I want you to go back to England and tell your father I'll be in touch with him when I'm ready, and not a moment before.'

Rachel gasped. 'Why don't you tell him yourself? There are such things as phones, you know. Even in paradise.'

Her mother's face contorted. 'Don't try to be clever with

me, Rachel. I know what you're doing. You and your father. You're trying to turn Matt and his family against me.'

'That's not true!' Rachel was appalled.

'It is true.' Sara spoke forcefully. 'And it's not going to work. They want me here. Matt wants me here. And I want to stay.'

Rachel couldn't believe her mother could be so obtuse. 'That wasn't the impression I got,' she murmured in a low voice. 'Please, Mum—'

'Don't call me that.'

'All right—Sara, then.' Rachel felt as if she was talking to a stranger. 'You know Dad loves you. I love you. Why don't you go home?'

Sara scowled. 'You see!' she exclaimed triumphantly. 'You *do* want to come between us.'

'Mum—Sara—Mr Brody didn't seem very pleased to see you last night. Surely—?'

'Jacob's just jealous, that's all.'

'Jealous!' Rachel wondered how much worse it could get. 'Mr Brody's not interested in you.'

'Did I say he was?'

Rachel was confused. 'You said he was jealous.'

'Yes. And he is. Jealous of my relationship with our son.'

Rachel felt sick now. 'Your—your son?' she whispered faintly.

'That's right.' Sara regarded her with suddenly critical eyes. 'Are you feeling all right? You've gone very pale suddenly.'

'I'm—I'm all right.'

Rachel didn't know how she got the words past the bile rising in her throat. But somehow she must not break down in front of this woman who had suddenly devastated her world.

'Well, if you're sure…'

'I'm sure.'

Rachel nodded, and her mother made an impatient little gesture as the waiter arrived with the coffee she'd ordered.

'Thank you,' she said shortly. And then, squaring her shoulders, she went on, 'You don't understand any of this, do you? I don't know what your father told you, but it obviously wasn't the truth.'

Rachel stared at her with disbelieving eyes. 'Does—does Dad know the truth?'

'About Matt? Of course he does.' Sara was dismissive. 'He's known for the last thirty-two years.'

Rachel couldn't speak. Nausea was rising in her throat now, and she was very much afraid she was going to throw up all over the breakfast table.

'I—excuse me,' she said abruptly, and, pushing up from the table, fled across the patio to the lobby and the public restrooms she'd seen there. She made it to the nearest cubicle with only seconds to spare. Her stomach heaved and she was violently sick.

She was still hanging over the bowl when she heard someone else come into the restroom. Praying it wasn't her mother, she remained silent, but Sara was no fool.

'Rachel?' she called. 'Is that you? What's wrong? What did your father tell you, for heaven's sake? Wait until I see him. I'll tell him exactly what I think of him, sending you out here to do his dirty work for him.'

Rachel sagged. She wanted to say her father hadn't sent her here for any underhand purpose, but that was no longer true. He'd known who Matt was when he'd sent her to find her mother. In God's name, why hadn't he told her the truth?

That Matt wasn't her mother's lover. He was Rachel's brother!

Rachel groaned and pulled a strip of toilet paper from the roll. Then she blew her nose. She was very near to tears, but she knew she had to behave as if it was her father who had upset her and no one else.

Flushing the toilet again, she unlocked the door and opened it. She was sure she must look like death warmed over, and she could only hope that her mother would put her nausea down to physical rather than emotional causes.

'What's wrong with you?' As Rachel went to wash her hands at the basin her mother regarded her suspiciously. 'What did you have for dinner last night? Something's upset you and I can't believe it's anything I've said.'

Rachel had to suppress a gulp of anguish. How blind could her mother be? After everything that had been said, she still had no conception of how her daughter was feeling.

'I—perhaps it was the French toast I had for breakfast,' she mumbled. And then, realising her mother was quite capable of reporting this, she added, 'Or maybe it's just a cold in my stomach. They say sunburn can do that. Chill you, you know.'

'Y-e-s.' Sara dragged the word out. 'Maybe.' She frowned. 'Do you want to go back to the table?'

'Heavens, no!'

Rachel shook her head violently, and then wished she hadn't when the room swam around her. But her response had been clear enough and her mother nodded.

'I suggest we go up to your room,' she said.

'I—my bag—'

'I'll get it.' For the first time Sara showed her a little consideration. 'What's the number of your room? I'll meet you there.'

The last thing Rachel wanted was for her mother to invade the only private space she had. But, short of admitting this, she had no choice. She gave her mother the number, and then left the restroom to hurry up the stairs to her room.

Now she prayed she wouldn't see Matt. Dear God, she hoped she never had to see him again...

CHAPTER THIRTEEN

RACHEL managed to get a seat on that evening's flight out of Jamaica.

The small inter-island plane that flew between St Antoine and Montego Bay connected with the large jet that would transport her to London, and Rachel had been relieved to find she had to leave for the airport before noon.

Sara Claiborne had been quite happy to use her local knowledge to get her daughter on board the propeller-driven aircraft, obviously as eager as Rachel was to get her off the island.

Rachel knew her mother thought she was leaving because she'd found out that her father's reason for sending her here had been a lie. The idea that her daughter's relationship with Matt might have something to do with her desire to leave didn't seem to occur to her. She didn't even question the fact that Rachel seemed in no hurry to get know her new brother.

Rachel shuddered at the thought. Thank God Matt had evidently had other matters to attend to that morning. By the time he realised she was gone she'd be off the island.

Yet, for all that, the day had dragged. Rachel didn't honestly know how she got through it. Allowing Sara into her bedroom, the room where she and Matt had first acknowledged their attraction to one another, had been harrowing, and pretending that the reason her stomach was upset was due to a chill, had torn her apart.

What she'd really wanted to do was lock herself away somewhere and cry like a baby. She was desolate, devastated, and no one—particularly not her mother—could comfort her.

Fortunately, Sara had been too wrapped up in her own affairs to notice her daughter's condition. And it had soon become obvious from her conversation that she was jealous of anyone who spent any time with her son.

She hadn't explained how Matt had come to be living with his father. All she'd said was that she'd made a terrible mistake in giving him up. She'd glossed over the details of her son's birth, giving the impression that the Brodys were to blame for what had happened.

In all honesty Rachel had hardly listened to her. She didn't want to hear that Jacob Brody had seduced her mother and then gone ahead and married someone else. Diana, she assumed. The whole situation was anathema to her, and she just wanted to put the whole damning episode behind her.

She didn't really relax until the big jet lifted off from the airport at Montego Bay. There'd been a two-hour delay between planes, and she'd been terrified Matt might discover what she'd done and come after her.

But no one came after her; no one spoke to her. She'd sat in the comfortable Club lounge and her attitude had evidently deterred any would-be acquaintance from approaching her.

The plane was due to land at Heathrow soon after eight o'clock the next morning, and although she would have preferred to make her own way home Rachel felt obliged to give her father the chance to meet her, if he wanted to.

She phoned him a couple of hours before they were due to land. And, even taking into account that she'd got him out of bed, Ralph Claiborne was shocked to hear from her.

'Why didn't you phone me before you left?' he demanded. 'Have you seen your mother? I must say I've been expecting you to ring for days.'

Rachel didn't want to get into that on the phone, particularly not on the plane, with half a dozen waking passengers more than interested to hear what she was saying.

'I'll tell you all about it when I see you,' she said. 'Don't worry about it. I can get a taxi home.'

'I wouldn't dream of letting you wait for a taxi,' he exclaimed. She could imagine him checking the clock as he spoke. 'You're due to land in a couple of hours, you say? That should give me time to get there.'

'Dad, it's the rush hour.'

'Don't be silly. I know a few short-cuts. I'll be there.'

Rachel shook her head. 'Okay.'

'Love you,' he said in farewell, but Rachel couldn't answer him.

Ignoring her fellow passengers, she folded the phone, drew her legs up to her chest and rested her chin on her knees. It was still dark outside the plane, dark and lonely, and for the first time since leaving St Antoine she allowed herself to think about Matt.

What was he thinking? she wondered. He must have discovered she'd left the island by now. Not that it would be any surprise to him, she thought painfully. If her mother had told him what she'd told her daughter, he would know how devastated Rachel must feel.

She didn't want to think about Matt's part in this, but it was difficult to avoid it. Hadn't it bothered him at *all* that their relationship was taboo? Or, like her, had he felt that irresistible compulsion? A compulsion that she now knew was forbidden.

A choking sob rose in her throat.

Oh, God, how could she bear it? Just twenty-four hours ago they'd been together. Twenty-four hours ago she'd been happier than she'd ever been in her life before.

Wrapping her arms around herself, she felt the hot tears welling in her eyes, spilling over. Tears streamed down her cheeks, dripping onto her arms, salty rivulets trickling into her mouth. She would never get over this, never. In just a few short days he'd turned her world around. He meant so much to her now. She cared about him. She *loved* him.

And it was so wrong.

Oh, God!

'Are you all right, Ms Claiborne?' One of the cabin staff had noticed her distress and was now hovering over her, blocking her from public view.

Rachel sniffed, trying to pull herself together. She had a tissue in the pocket of her jeans and she struggled to get it out. It tore as she did so, and she smeared a hand across her burning face.

'Sorry,' she mumbled, realising she was hardly an advertisement for the airline. 'I'm just feeling a bit emotional, that's all.' She sniffed again. 'Family problems, you know?'

The girl frowned and handed her a handful of tissues taken from the drinks trolley. 'Are you sure?'

'Oh, yes.' Rachel thanked her for the tissues and used them to dry her eyes. 'Have we much further to go?'

'Just over an hour.' The girl hesitated. 'Can I get you something to drink? A vodka and tonic, perhaps?'

Rachel managed a faint smile. 'At six o'clock in the morning?' she said humorously. 'I don't think so.'

'Well, if you change your mind...'

'Thanks.' Rachel sniffed again. 'I appreciate your concern.'

And she did. In a few words the attendant had shown her more sympathy than her mother. It hadn't even occurred to Sara Claiborne to question whether Rachel was fit to travel over four thousand miles when she'd been so sick.

But that was okay. Rachel reminded herself firmly. Her mother's sympathy was something she could do without.

It was a quarter to nine by the time she cleared passport control and collected her luggage from the carousel. But Ralph Claiborne was waiting patiently just outside Customs, and, despite the feeling of betrayal she still felt, Rachel didn't hesitate before going into his arms. The real reason he'd sent her to St Antoine, the lies he'd told her about her mother, mattered less at that moment than the exquisite sense of security she felt when his familiar arms closed about her.

She couldn't help herself then. She started crying again, and her father drew back in some alarm, gazing at her with anxious eyes. 'Rachel?' he said questioningly, but she just shook her head.

'Not now, Dad,' she said, and although she knew he would have liked an explanation he seemed to realise she was on the edge of a complete breakdown.

A couple of hours later, at her parents' apartment, with the cup of filtered coffee her father had made in her hand, Rachel knew she couldn't prevaricate any longer.

'Why didn't you tell me you knew who Matt Brody really was?' she asked, controlling the urge to rail at him. 'You let me think Mum was having an affair with him.'

'I know.' Ralph Claiborne didn't try to deny it. He seated himself opposite her at the kitchen table. 'But if I'd told you it was Jacob Brody I was worried about, I'd have had to explain who Matthew Brody was.'

Rachel blinked. 'And that would have been a problem? How?'

'Oh, Rachel, haven't you realised yet? That wasn't my secret to tell.'

'So you admit it was a secret?'

'Your mother's secret, yes.'

Rachel shook her head. 'And what do you mean, you were worried about Mum and Jacob Brody? Matt's father's happily married.'

'Is he?'

'Yes.'

'You've met him?'

'Yes.'

'But I understand he had a stroke a couple of months ago?'

'He did, yes.' Rachel was confused. 'What does that have to do with anything?'

Her father sighed. 'You'll have realised that he and your mother knew one another many years ago?'

'Well, she didn't tell me, but yes,' said Rachel heavily. 'So?'

'Oh, Rachel, I shouldn't be telling you this. She should.'

'But she's not here, is she?' said Rachel, struggling to keep her own feelings at bay. 'Please, Dad, I need to know. Why was I never told there was someone else before you? That she had another child?'

Ralph rested an elbow on the table and cupped his chin in his hand. 'Because—well, because from what I've gathered over the years it wasn't like that.'

'*What* wasn't like that?' Rachel was confused.

'Let me start at the beginning.' Her father took a steadying breath. 'First of all, when I got to know your mother, she told me that she'd had a baby. She knew we were getting serious about one another, and she wanted there to be no secrets between us.'

Rachel stared at him. 'So how young was she when she had—the baby?'

'Sixteen.'

'Sixteen!' Rachel was incredulous.

'Yes, sixteen. She and her parents had taken a holiday on St Antoine, and during the course of their stay she got to know Jacob Brody.'

He paused again, and then continued, 'I believe he was a few years older than she was—twenty, or thereabouts. But your mother was quite open about the way she'd pursued him. And over the two weeks she'd allowed him to—well—'

'I get the picture,' said Rachel tersely. 'Go on.'

'Of course when she got back home and found she was pregnant she was terrified. Things were very different in those days, and there was no question of her becoming a single mother. As I understand it, her father wrote to Jacob's father and told him of the situation. And in a matter of weeks it was decided that when the baby was born Jacob Brody would become its legal guardian.'

So that was what Matt had meant when he'd told her he'd been born in England, but had lived all his life on the island.

'You and Mum got married when she was nineteen, didn't you?'

'That's right.' Her father nodded. 'And to begin with we were very happy.'

'But?'

He sighed. 'I suppose you were about thirteen years old when she told me she'd kept track of Matthew's life for the past eighteen years. I thought at first she'd kept in touch with Jacob Brody, but after what you've just told me I doubt it. But somehow, maybe via a third party, she'd learned that Matthew was going to go to Princeton University that autumn. She told me she wanted to get in touch with him, to go and see him, to try and mend the rift between them.'

'Oh, Dad!'

'Yes.' He sounded weary now. 'It was a shock. I don't deny it. Her own parents were dead by that time. You remember they were killed in that train accident when you were twelve years old? Maybe she'd been thinking about it since then. I don't think Sara would have done anything against her parents' wishes, but after they were dead...'

'So did she go?'

'Oh, yes. According to her, Matthew was delighted to see her. Somehow I doubt that, too, but anyway, he didn't turn her away. I know Jacob Brody wasn't too happy about the arrangement. He and his wife regarded themselves as Matthew's parents. There was an exchange of letters in which he voiced his disapproval. But Matthew was above the age of consent, and I'm sure your mother had taken that into consideration when she made her move.'

Rachel was appalled. 'And has she seen him since then?'

'A couple of times,' agreed her father flatly. 'You remember that trip to Paris she made with your aunt Laura? That was to see Matthew. Then once she flew out to Miami and met him there.'

'But not to St Antoine?'

'Not until now.' Ralph Claiborne sighed again. 'That's what worried me so much. She'd heard that Matthew's father had had a heart attack or a stroke, or some such thing, and she told me she wanted to be with Matthew, to comfort him at this time.'

'But you didn't believe her.'

'No.' Her father was honest. 'Rachel, Jacob Brody is her son's father! No one has a stronger hold on her affections than him.'

Rachel was bewildered. 'But you're *my* father.' She thought she might cry again. 'Don't I mean anything to her at all?'

'Oh, Rachel, of course you do.' Ralph leaned across the table and covered her hand with both of his. 'We both love you very much. You know that.'

'But a son means so much more. Is that it?'

'No.' Her father was looking worried again now. 'Oh, Rachel, dear, don't press me. Your mother has her own way of doing things, as you should know. She'd never forgive me if I started rocking the boat now.'

Rachel couldn't believe it. Pushing herself up from the table, she said, 'Don't you think she's the one who's rocking the boat, Dad?' She gazed at him despairingly. 'She's talking about staying on the island. She says she wants to be with Matt. What else does she have to do before you realise we come a very low second on her list?'

Ralph gazed up at her with anxious eyes. 'She said that? She said she wants to stay on St Antoine?'

'Well...' Rachel had to be completely honest. 'She said she was happy there. She didn't say she wasn't coming back, but she didn't say she was either.'

'Damn her!'

It was the first time she'd heard her father swear in connection with her mother. She knew they'd had arguments from time to time, but her father had always moderated his language in her presence. Now, however, he seemed almost desperate in his need to voice his feelings. Rachel felt guilty for being the one to burst whatever bubble he'd been living in, but he had to know what her mother was thinking. He had to know there was a chance she might not come back.

A sudden knock at the kitchen door had them both lifting their heads in surprise. 'It's only me, Ralph,' called a light feminine voice, and Rachel's aunt Laura opened the door and came confidently into the room.

'Oh, Rachel!' she exclaimed when she saw her niece, and Rachel guessed she was the last person Laura had expected to see. 'I didn't know you were due back today.'

'She wasn't,' said Ralph heavily. 'Apparently your sister is considering staying in St Antoine, so Rachel decided to come home.'

That wasn't quite how it had been, but Rachel was happy to allow him that concession at least.

Laura gasped, however. She was a pretty woman, a few years younger than her sister, and plumper. 'You're not serious?' she exclaimed. 'Oh, that silly woman! I mean—'

She broke off abruptly, looking to Ralph as if for guidance, and her brother-in-law ran a heavy hand down his face. 'Rachel knows about Matthew,' he said. 'Sara's told her.'

'Oh...' Laura appeared relieved. 'Well, anyway, Matthew's what? Thirty-five? Thirty-six? He won't want his mother on his back for the rest of his life.'

'Tell me about it.' Ralph got to his feet and lifted his shoulders in a weary gesture. Then, forcing his thoughts into other channels, he nodded his head towards the dish she was holding. 'What's that you've got there?'

'Oh, it's just a casserole I made for your supper,' said Laura deprecatingly, looking apologetically at Rachel. Then, as if some explanation was necessary, she continued, 'Your father gave me a key so I could get in and tidy the place while he was at work. Obviously I didn't expect him to be home this morning. Or you either,' she added. She forced a smile. 'Did you have a good trip? Or is that a silly question?'

'It's a silly question,' grunted Ralph.

Rachel, who was beginning to feel like a third wheel, said, 'I'll just use the bathroom, Dad. Then I'll go back to my apartment. I dare say I've got some tidying up to do before I go back to work.'

'You could stay here,' suggested her father, but Rachel shook her head.

'No, I couldn't.' She smiled at Laura. 'Excuse me.'

Her father patted her shoulder as she passed him, but Rachel didn't have the strength to return the gesture. It hurt a little to know that even her aunt had known about Matt's existence, but obviously she would. When Sara had been pursuing Jacob, Laura wouldn't even have reached her teens. But she'd definitely have been old enough to know her sister was pregnant.

She went into the bathroom that adjoined her parents' bedroom. She wasn't surprised to see how pale she was. She was surprised her aunt hadn't commented on it. But then, she suspected Laura had had enough to do, making excuses for running after her father while her mother was away. Sara needed to get home soon, before her sister took over her husband as well as her home.

The urge to cry again swept over her, and she stifled a groan. Dear heaven, she felt as if her whole metabolism was breaking down. She never cried; not normally. But then again, these were hardly normal times.

She was walking back along the hall again when she heard her name mentioned. Not by her father, this time, but by her aunt.

'You didn't tell Rachel the truth?' she was saying, her voice full of impatience. 'Oh, Ralph, the girl's thirty, for goodness' sake! I don't care what Sara thinks. She deserves to know!'

CHAPTER FOURTEEN

DON GRAHAM stopped by Rachel's desk on his way back to his office.

'Rachel,' he said, and for once there was no trace of censure in his tone—which hadn't been the case for the past three weeks.

Since her return to work, he'd seemed to be constantly on her case, and she couldn't exactly blame him. Her concentration was spotty, at best, and she knew her work was suffering.

But what could she do? Her whole world seemed to have tilted on its axis, and although the relief of learning that Matt wasn't her brother was paramount in her thoughts, the knowledge that he'd known the truth all along put an entirely different complexion on their relationship.

Which was good—and bad.

Thanks to Aunt Laura's intervention, she now knew that she'd been adopted by the Claibornes when she was only a few days old. Her biological mother had been a law student, who'd had no intention of keeping the baby in any case, but who had died from a blood infection soon after the birth. She'd been unmarried, and no one seemed to know who Rachel's father had been. Another student seemed the most likely solution.

Sara's reasons for keeping this from her daughter seemed selfish, in retrospect, but Rachel wasn't into judging anyone. It had been common enough in the past for parents to keep their child's adopted status a secret, and after what Sara must have suffered when her son was taken from her there was some justification for her decision.

After the first initial shock Rachel had been prepared to be generous. She believed her father when he said he would have told her sooner, and, after all, he'd suffered enough in his own way.

Not that he seemed to be suffering now, she acknowledged. Aunt Laura was making herself a very satisfactory substitute so far as a housekeeper was concerned. It was to be hoped her mother knew what she was doing, Rachel mused ruefully. Laura might just try to dislodge her sister in a far more intimate way.

And as for Matt...

Well, if it hadn't been for Matt there wouldn't have been this dilemma. For her, or her mother.

But Matt was a factor. Rachel knew in her heart of hearts that if she'd known the truth she'd never have left the island as she had. And it would be so easy to blame Sara for that, too.

God knew what he must think of her. Would her mother have explained that so far as Rachel had been aware he was her brother? Or would that have been too much like admitting defeat? And, in any case, Sara had no idea how far their relationship had gone.

So far as Matt as concerned Rachel had left without even saying goodbye. And after what they'd shared that must seem the deepest cut of all.

Or perhaps not. She didn't know how Matt felt about her. Yes, he'd been attracted to her. Yes, he'd made love to her. But he must have made love to dozens of women, and surely if he'd really cared about her he'd have come after her. Just because she'd instinctively known that he was going to be the love of her life it did not mean that he felt the same. Obviously he didn't.

'Rachel?'

Don Graham was still standing beside her desk, and Rachel realised that once again her thoughts had been wandering.

Colour stained her cheeks. 'I'm sorry.' She pushed back her chair and got awkwardly to her feet. 'Did you want me, Don?'

The possibility that he was thinking of dismissing her crossed her mind. And who could blame him? Her work definitely wasn't up to standard. She hadn't signed up any new accounts for the past three weeks.

'You've got a visitor,' he said in a calming voice. 'It's your mother.'

Rachel stared at him in disbelief. She and her father had been getting used to the fact that Sara Claiborne would return home when she was ready and not before. And her father had said nothing about her mother coming home when she'd phoned him the night before.

'Yes, your mother,' said Don Graham kindly, squeezing her arm. 'Look, your dad's told me she's been staying with friends, and that there's been something of an upset in the family. But she's here now, and she seems eager to speak to you.'

Rachel swallowed, glancing across the office to where a wall of frosted glass hid the reception area. Her mother was here? At the *Chingford Herald*? To see her? Why?

'I've told Valerie to put her in the interview room,' went on Don Graham evenly. 'I'm sure you have lots to talk about, so I'm giving you the rest of the day off. It's Friday. I'll see you again on Monday. Okay?'

Rachel was tempted to say no, it wasn't okay. Why should she be available when her mother wanted her, when for the past few weeks she hadn't heard a word from her?

But she wasn't that kind of person. Whatever her mother wanted, whatever reason her father had had for keeping her return a secret, she had to deal with it.

'Okay,' she said in a low voice, aware that once again she was attracting attention from the people around her. 'Thank you.'

Don Graham merely arched his brows and walked away, and, feeling much like a condemned woman on her way to the scaffold, Rachel walked slowly towards the office door.

Sara Claiborne was seated at the table in the interview room. Someone, probably Valerie, had supplied her with a mug of coffee, but she had barely touched it. And as soon as she saw her daughter she rose immediately to her feet.

'Oh, Rachel,' she said, and there was a break in her voice. 'I've been such a fool!'

Rachel closed the door behind her and leaned back against it. Despite fair warning, she found that seeing her mother again had made her legs feel decidedly wobbly. And, although she was sure Sara would have appreciated a hug, too much had happened to allow her to expose her emotions once again.

Squaring her shoulders, she said instead, 'Dad didn't tell me you were back.'

'That's because your father doesn't know yet,' said her mother heavily. 'I just flew in this morning and came straight here. I guessed you'd be at work and I needed to speak to you.' She paused. 'Alone.'

Rachel pushed away from the door. 'Well, don't you think you ought to ring Dad first? He's been really worried about you.'

'I'm sure your aunt Laura's been looking after him,' said Sara, somewhat cynically.

'Well, you can't blame Dad for that.'

Sara sighed. 'I'm not blaming anyone, Rachel. Except perhaps myself.' She spread an arm. 'Look, can we go somewhere we can have a private conversation? I never trust newspaper offices. They have microphones everywhere.'

Rachel shook her head. 'How about McMillan Court?' she

asked, naming the complex where her parents' apartment was situated. 'It's private there.'

Her mother hesitated. 'Couldn't we go to your apartment, Rachel? I don't want us to be interrupted.'

Rachel bit her lip. It was true that although her father would be at work Aunt Laura had a key, and might well be doing a little housework in his absence.

'All right,' she said at last. She glanced at her watch. 'There's a bus in fifteen minutes.'

'We'll get a cab,' said Sara firmly, bending to pick up her handbag, and Rachel suddenly noticed the suitcase standing behind the door.

'Okay,' she said, reaching for the handle of the case. 'I'll just get my things.'

Traffic being what it was, it took them almost an hour to reach Rachel's apartment. An older complex than the one where her parents lived, it was nevertheless equipped with all the usual amenities. A lift transported them to the seventh floor, and Rachel opened the door to number 702.

Not surprisingly, perhaps, her mother had said little in the taxi. There was a definite rift between them, and although they'd spoken about the weather, and the contrast between the chilly March day outside the windows and the heat of St Antoine, they were casual comments that anyone might have made.

Once they stepped inside Rachel's apartment, however, she heard her mother breathe a sigh of relief before collapsing somewhat ungracefully onto the sofa in the living room. Sara leaned back and closed her eyes, and for the first time Rachel allowed herself to notice that the years her mother had appeared to shed in St Antoine had returned, with interest.

Grey streaks were appearing in her hair again, and beneath her fur-lined jacket her flared woollen trousers and crew-necked sweater were anything but flamboyant. She looked pale, and tired, and when she opened her eyes again Rachel was amazed to see they were filled with tears.

'Oh, Mum,' she exclaimed, starting towards her, sympathy for the woman who'd raised her overcoming any resentment she'd been feeling. But her mother's next words halted her in her tracks.

'Matt and I have had such a terrible row,' she said brokenly, tears starting to trickle down her cheeks. She sniffed noisily. 'He hates me. I know he does. Oh, Rachel, why did you ever go to St Antoine?'

Rachel sat down rather abruptly on the arm of the nearest chair. 'Why did I ever go to St Antoine?' she echoed faintly. 'You know why I went, Mum. I was looking for you.'

'Oh, I know that.' Sara was testy. Sitting up, she reached into her handbag for a tissue. 'I know why you went there, you silly girl. I want to know what you think it had to do with you?'

Rachel's jaw sagged. 'Mum—Dad was worried about you. I was worried about you. We didn't know what to think.'

'Your father thought I'd gone there to see Jacob, didn't he?' Sara spoke impatiently. 'As if I would. But he had no right to send you there, involving you in my affairs.'

Rachel straightened her spine. 'So why don't you take this up with Dad?' Any sympathy she'd been feeling had quickly fled. 'I can't imagine why you would come here to talk to me.'

'Can't you? *Can't you?*' Her mother stared at her. 'Didn't you hear what I said? Matt and I have had a terrible row.' She swallowed convulsively. 'About you!'

'Me?' Rachel was glad she was sitting down at that moment. She didn't think her legs would have supported her. But she had to ask the obvious question. 'Why?'

'Oh, don't be coy.' Sara was contemptuous. 'I know what's been going on—don't you understand? Between you and Matt.' She paused. 'He told me.'

Rachel didn't know what to think. She couldn't think of any occasion when she might have come under discussion between Matt and her mother.

Unless…

'Well?' Sara was waiting for her to speak. 'Don't you have anything to say for yourself?' She shook her head. 'I must say when he first told me I could hardly believe it.'

Rachel stiffened. 'Why? Because you don't think I'm good enough for him?'

'Oh, don't be so silly.' Her mother wasn't having that. 'No. No. It's just you've always been such a—such a—'

'Recluse?'

'No.' Sara sighed. 'But you've always kept men at a distance.'

Rachel shrugged. There was nothing to say to that.

'I can only assume that you allowed the island—and Matt, of course—to go to your head.'

Rachel's lips twisted. 'Something like that.'

Sara shook her head. 'It didn't bother you that to all intents and purposes he was your brother?'

'How dare you say that?' Rachel was horrified. 'My God, I didn't even know he was your son. I thought you and he were—were—'

'No!' Sara stared up at her, aghast. 'You can't have thought that a man like Matt would be interested in someone of my age.' Her lips curled. 'He barely acknowledges me as his mother.'

'Whose fault is that?' Rachel knew her words were hurtful, but her mother had hurt her, too. 'I think you'd better go.'

'Not yet.' Sara got to her feet. 'There's something you need to know.'

'What?' Rachel was contemptuous now. 'If you're going to tell me that I was adopted, don't bother. I already know.'

'You know?' Evidently this was what Sara had intended

to say. Rachel wondered why she'd suddenly decided to tell her the truth. After all these years, it was incredible.

'How did you find out?'

Rachel shrugged. 'I heard Dad and Aunt Laura talking. Does it matter? I know now. You can save your confession for someone else.'

Sara caught her breath. 'Don't be cruel, Rachel. You don't know what I've had to suffer all these years. But I might have known Laura wouldn't be able to keep her mouth shut. She's never understood what it's been like for me.'

'And what about Dad?' demanded Rachel. 'Don't you think he's suffered, too?'

'But Matt's my son, Rachel.'

'And you've never let Dad forget it, have you?'

Sara bent her head. 'I thought I'd have other children,' she said. 'I wanted at least three. But—well—we discovered your father had a problem. That was why I agreed to an adoption.'

'And you got me,' said Rachel bitterly. 'How disappointing for you.'

'Oh, don't say that.' Her mother heaved a sigh. 'Look, Rachel, I know we've never been as close as a mother and daughter should be, but I loved you. I *love* you. You must know that.'

'But not as much as you love Matt,' said Rachel sadly. 'I really think you'd better go, Mum. Just pray Dad has more sympathy for you than I do right now.'

'702 Lincoln Place.'

Matt murmured the words in an undertone as he stood looking up at the tall apartment building.

So this was where Rachel lived, he mused, trying to suppress the sense of trepidation he felt at invading her space without an invitation. What if he'd been mistaken? What if she really didn't want to see him again? At barely eight o'clock on a Saturday morning she probably wasn't even awake, let alone up and dressed.

Still, he hadn't flown all this way just to turn back at the first obstacle. He had to see her; he needed to see her. He had to know what his mother had said to her. Dear God, had she really let the girl go on thinking she was his sister?

He hadn't found out that Rachel didn't know she was adopted until Thursday evening. He'd always known Sara had an adopted daughter. She'd made a point of telling him that she wasn't Rachel's biological mother.

He'd naturally assumed she'd told Rachel the same. Discovering that she hadn't had put a whole new slant on Rachel's reasons for leaving, and he'd wanted to strangle his mother for causing such a tangled skein of grief.

God, how could she do it? Knowing he was attracted to Rachel? Was that why? Was she so jealous of anyone who got close to him that she'd go to any lengths to protect herself?

He'd been shattered when he'd found out Rachel had left the island, and his mother had known that. But she hadn't said a word about speaking to her daughter before she left.

Naturally he'd blamed himself. He'd been sure Rachel must have had second thoughts. She'd seemed so fragile, so vulnerable; a virgin, for heaven's sake. And he'd plunged into a full-blown affair. He'd convinced himself that she hadn't been prepared to continue their relationship on those terms and for the past three weeks he'd buried his misery in work.

Then, on Thursday evening, he'd had dinner with his father. Diana had been attending a meeting of her music festival committee, and Amalie had been out with her boyfriend. So there had been just the two of them.

Jacob was getting stronger every day, but to Matt's surprise seemed quite content with the way his son was handling the business.

'I'm beginning to enjoy researching my book,' he'd confessed ruefully. 'Perhaps I'm getting lazy in my old age. All I need now is an assistant to translate my notes into some kind of coherent language.'

Matt smiled, but he wasn't really in the mood to discuss his father's occupation. He was finding it harder every day to conduct even a civil conversation with his employees, and this taciturnity did not go unremarked.

'Sara still giving you a hard time?' asked his father understandingly. 'When is that woman going to go home?'

'God knows.' Matt pushed his steak aside and lay back in his chair. 'I think she believes I want her here. But she couldn't be more wrong.'

'It's a pity Rachel couldn't stay longer,' remarked Jacob thoughtfully. 'You and she seemed to get along so well. She's a lovely girl.'

Matt's lips tightened. 'Yes, she is.'

'It's a shame that you and she are related. In other circumstances—'

'Related?' Matt stared at his father.

'Well, you do have the same mother,' Jacob pointed out mildly. 'I mean—'

'We don't have the same mother,' Matt interrupted him sharply. 'Why would you say a thing like that? You *know* Rachel was adopted by the Claibornes.'

Jacob's jaw dropped. 'No, I didn't know that.' He shook his head. 'How could I? You and I hardly talk about your mother, goodness knows, let alone her daughter.'

'But—' Matt straightened in his chair. 'Sara must have mentioned it.'

'No. No, she hasn't.' Jacob was very definite about that. 'It's not the sort of thing she would tell me, now, is it?'

'My God!' Matt pushed back his chair and got to his feet. A terrible suspicion was stirring in his gut. 'Do you think Rachel knows she's adopted?'

Jacob shrugged. 'Who knows? You'd have to ask your mother. Why? Is it important?'

Matt gave a mirthless laugh. 'It could be.' He raked back his hair with fingers that weren't quite steady. 'I slept with her.'

Jacob's astonishment was evident. 'You slept with Rachel?'

'Yeah.' Matt paced restlessly across the floor. 'I never even thought that she might not know about her adoption.'

Jacob frowned. 'But if she didn't know she was adopted, what was she doing sleeping with you? If she thought you were her brother...'

Matt shook his head. 'Because she didn't know Sara was my mother. She thought Sara and I were an item,' he said bitterly. 'I knew what she thought and I played upon it.'

'Why?'

'Because I wanted to make her jealous, I guess.' Matt was impatient. 'Does it matter? The fact is, she had no idea I was Sara's son. I'm sure of that.'

'You sound very sure of her altogether,' murmured his father drily. 'Am I to understand that the hangdog expression you've worn for the last few weeks isn't just because your mother is still staying at Mango Key?'

Matt gazed ruefully at him. 'Yeah, yeah,' he admitted frustratedly. 'Call me a fool, if you like, but I've never met a girl like Rachel before.'

Jacob returned his stare. 'It sounds serious.' He paused. 'So why haven't you done anything about it before now?'

Matt bent his head. 'I had my reasons.'

'Not wholly commendable ones, by the sound of it,' observed his father, and when his son didn't answer, he continued, 'What are you going to do?'

Matt blew out a breath. 'I'm going to go and get the truth out of Sara,' he said, nodding. He made an apologetic gesture. 'Sorry about leaving you to it.' He grimaced. 'I've just lost my appetite.'

'You didn't have much of an appetite to begin with.' Jacob

was resigned. 'Yes, go. This is far more important than wasting good steak.'

Matt remembered he'd driven the distance between Jaracoba and Mango Key in record time. And, looking back, he was fairly sure his mother had had some suspicion of why he was home so early even before he'd asked her the burning question.

She'd prevaricated at first, but one look at his grim face had warned her not to lie to him. Using tears as an ally, she'd tried to tell him that losing him as a baby had had a devastating effect on her life. Then, discovering her husband was sterile, she'd only agreed to adoption as a last resort.

'But you never told Rachel you and her father weren't her biological parents?'

'I didn't think it was important,' she'd exclaimed appealingly. 'It wasn't something people talked about in those days. And I don't know why you're getting so chewed up about it now. Rachel means nothing to you.'

'Doesn't she?'

Matt recalled how he'd stared at her until she'd dropped her eyes, and he'd known in that moment that Sara knew exactly what she'd done.

The row that had followed had been brutal. But, dammit, he'd been half afraid—was still half afraid, if he was honest— that his mother had screwed up any chance of his making a life with Rachel. And if that happened he'd never forgive her.

Never.

CHAPTER FIFTEEN

'702.'

Matt said the number to himself as he scanned the keypad situated beside the glass doors. Evidently, with so many occupants, an individual bell system wasn't feasible, and visitors were expected to key in the number of the apartment they wanted.

He was hesitating over whether to select Rachel's number or take a chance on someone else releasing the lock, when a young woman emerged from the building and kindly held the door open for him.

'Thanks,' he said, amazed that the idea of letting a thief into the block didn't occur to her. But maybe she thought he looked harmless enough.

'No problem,' she responded, with an inviting little smile, and Matt realised that she had another agenda entirely. 'Are you looking for someone? Perhaps I can help you.'

Matt's mouth compressed. 'My girlfriend,' he said pleasantly. 'But thanks for the offer.'

The girl's smile disappeared, and with a shrug she walked away. Matt glanced after her and then stifled a smile as he turned towards the lifts. One down and one to go, he thought wryly. If only Rachel would be so accommodating.

He stepped out of the lift onto a rubber-tiled floor. It wasn't luxurious, but it was clean and well-lit, with long windows at each end of the corridor allowing watery sunlight to stream into the hall.

Number 702 was two doors along. And, despite everything that had happened and his own determination to come here, Matt had to admit to a feeling of apprehension.

What if he'd been wrong? He had no real idea what Rachel might be thinking at this moment. Was it possible he'd misunderstood her reasons for leaving?

Dear God, he'd been devastated after that confrontation with his mother. His first impulse had been to get her out of his house, and the very next morning he moved her into the hotel. She'd protested, naturally, but he'd had enough. Then he'd gone to see his father.

As usual, Jacob Brody had been a pillar of strength, and Matt had spent the next twenty-four hours organising his schedule so he could leave the island for a few days. But when he'd gone to the hotel to tell his mother what he was going to do he'd discovered Sara had left the day before.

To say Matt had been angry at the news would have been an understatement. Particularly as it had been too late then for him to get to Montego Bay in time for that evening's flight. Instead, he'd contacted a friend who ran a charter service out of Kingston. He'd flown to London in the luxury of a private jet, mentally chastising himself for not realising his mother would want to get to Rachel first.

There was no bell, so he knocked at the door of number 702. It reminded him of that evening when he'd brought his grandmother's cream to treat Rachel's sunburn. But it also reminded him of what had happened when he'd touched her, and in spite of his nerves his body tightened in response.

There was an eyehole in this door, too, he noticed, and he wondered if Rachel was staring through it right now, trying to decide whether she would speak to him. He had no idea if his mother had been to see her, or what she might have said to her. Sara could easily had lied and claimed he hadn't known that Rachel was adopted either. Hell, would a mother really do something like that to her daughter, adopted or otherwise? He prayed not.

When he heard a key turning in the lock and a chain being released, he felt a wave of perspiration break out on the back of his neck. He'd never been so nervous, he realised. God, she'd really messed with his mind.

The door opened a few inches, and he glimpsed the woman who'd come to mean so much to him hovering just beyond the threshold. She wasn't dressed. Well, not dressed as he was used to seeing her, but he wasn't complaining. The cropped tee shirt and what looked like men's boxers displayed a delicate wedge of porcelain skin at her midriff and almost the whole length of those gorgeous legs.

'Matt,' she said, and he was heartened that she didn't slam the door in his face. 'Wh—What are you doing here?'

'Would you believe, sightseeing?' he asked, trying for humour. But he was honestly weary, and it didn't quite come off. 'I guess not.' He grimaced and rested one hand against the door frame. 'How about I've come to see you? Does that cover it?'

Rachel's pulse was racing. When she'd heard the knock at the door she'd been sure it wouldn't be anyone she knew. She didn't expect to see her mother again any time soon, and her father wouldn't call on her at eight o'clock on a Saturday morning.

Living in such a large block, she was used to people getting the wrong apartment, and she'd been quite prepared to ignore it.

Then, when she'd peered through the eyehole, she'd seen Matt and her legs had turned to jelly. Dear heaven, after what her mother had said she'd doubted she'd ever see him again.

'May I come in?'

He sounded tired, and Rachel immediately stepped to one

side to allow him through the doorway. He was wearing a long black cashmere overcoat, open over dark pants and a black tee shirt, and the hem of the coat brushed the lower part of her leg as he went by.

Rachel's breathing was suspended for a moment. And then she gathered herself sufficiently to grab the door and close it again, shutting the much cooler air out in the corridor.

The apartments comprised a small foyer leading into a large living-cum-dining room, with a small kitchen off to the side. But once again Matt's presence made the room seem much smaller, his dark maleness making her intensely aware of her own rumpled appearance.

'I'll just go and put some clothes on,' she began, but he held up a hand when she would have fled into her bedroom.

'No,' he said huskily. 'Don't.'

'But I look—'

'—beautiful the way you are,' Matt assured her, his green eyes shadowed by emotions she couldn't begin to fathom. 'Can we sit down?'

'Before you fall down, you mean?' Rachel knew a surge of anxiety, but she tried not show it. 'You look—exhausted.'

'Gee, thanks. And after I was so complimentary about you,' he remarked wryly.

'You just—well, you don't look as if you've been sleeping very well.' She gestured towards the sofa. 'Go ahead. Sit. I'll get you some coffee.'

'I don't need any coffee.' Matt's hand closed around her bare arm, his fingers dark against the lingering remains of her tan. 'Stay with me. We need to talk.'

'Yes.' Rachel agreed with him there. 'Mostly about what you're doing here.'

'I told you. I'm here because I had to see you.'

Rachel shook her head. 'It's been three weeks, Matt—'

'Do you think I don't know that?'

He spoke harshly, his fingers tightening painfully about

her wrist. Rachel had the feeling he was nearing the end of his tether. The anguish in his face wasn't simulated. He really did look worn out.

'Look, let me get you that coffee,' she said, urging him back towards the sofa. 'You relax, hmm? It won't take long.'

'I don't want any coffee,' Matt insisted, but to her relief he did release her arm and slip off his overcoat. He tossed it over the back of the sofa, then sank wearily onto the edge of the cushions. 'There. Will that do?'

Rachel pulled her bottom lip between her teeth. She couldn't help but be aware that his eyes were now on a level with the waistband of her shorts. Aware, too, of the revealing strip of midriff it exposed, and the pulse that was hammering in her throat.

'Okay.' Matt raked agitated fingers over his scalp. 'First of all, has Sara been here?'

Rachel hesitated. 'Ye-es.'

'God, I knew it!' Matt's eyes had darkened again and his exclamation was bitter. 'As soon as she realised what I would do, she high-tailed it back here—' He broke off. 'I'm assuming she told you—?'

He sighed, and, realising what he wanted to say, Rachel murmured, 'If you're meaning that I'm adopted, I already knew. I overheard my father and my aunt Laura talking. She was of the opinion that I should have been told years ago.'

'Thank God for Aunt Laura!' For the first time there was a trace of humour in Matt's face. 'I bet Sara was livid when she found out.'

'Matt…'

'Well…' He was unrepentant. 'When I think of what she's put me through!'

'What she's put *you* through?'

Rachel looked confused, but Matt only shook his head. 'I'll get to that,' he said unevenly. 'Let me tell you why I didn't come to find you before this, right?'

Rachel lifted her shoulders. 'If—if it's important.'

'What the hell is that supposed to mean?' She'd forgotten the precarious state of his emotions. He scowled. 'Of course it's important, dammit. It's the most important thing of all. What do you want to hear? That I can't eat? Can't sleep? That ever since you left I've been blaming myself for ruining your life?'

'Ruining my life?' Rachel stared at him in disbelief.

'Well, okay.' Matt conceded the point. 'Perhaps that was too melodramatic. But, hell, Rachel, you know what I'm getting at.' He paused, and then went on more calmly. 'You were a virgin. You didn't get that way by inviting jerks like me into your bed.'

'Jerks like you?'

'Yeah.' Matt groaned. 'I should have realised how innocent you were. I should have waited until we knew one another better. But—I couldn't keep my hands off you.' He gave a harsh laugh. 'Ironic, isn't it, when I criticised you for not trusting me?'

Rachel frowned now. 'You don't regret what happened?'

'Don't be crazy!'

'Then I don't—'

'I thought that was why you left the island without seeing me again,' Matt interrupted her harshly. He tipped back his head and stared up at the ceiling for a moment, as if he might find inspiration there. 'Do you have any idea how I felt when I arrived back at the hotel and found you'd checked out that morning?'

He looked at her again. 'Obviously not. Well, believe me, I was devastated. And the only reason I could come up with was that you regretted what I'd done and you didn't want to see me again.'

Rachel's jaw dropped. 'But didn't my mother—? Well, no, I suppose she wouldn't.'

'What?' Matt's gaze was intent. 'Tell me that perhaps she

knew why you'd left? Confide that she'd had a cosy little chat with you? Inform me that you thought I was your brother, even? Yeah, I think we both know Sara better than that.'

'Oh, Matt!' Giving in to the urge to be nearer to him, Rachel moved closer. 'And I've been thinking you were glad you didn't have to see me again.'

'How could you think that?' Matt reached for her then, his hands closing about the upper part of her thighs, pulling her between his legs. He leant towards her, pressing his face into the warm mound of her belly. 'That night we spent together was the best night of my entire life.'

'And—and mine,' whispered Rachel shakily, and Matt lifted his head to look up at her again.

'So, then, can I take it that you wouldn't have left the island if Sara hadn't spoken to you?' he demanded.

'Do you have to ask?' Rachel was trembling now.

'Maybe I just need to hear you say the words,' said Matt unsteadily, and the sensual quality of his gaze made her knees go weak.

'I wouldn't have left,' she admitted honestly. 'Not without seeing you again anyway.' She felt his thumbs invading the hem of her shorts and jerked uneasily. 'But you should have told me that Sara was your mother.'

'Yeah, I should.' Matt's eyes darkened. 'Though with hind-sight it's probably just as well I didn't, hmm? I mean—God, can you imagine how you'd have felt if *I'd* told you?'

Rachel let him pull her closer, until her knees were resting against the junction of his thighs. It was incredibly hard to think with the heat and the scent and the pure male strength of him surrounding her, so that all she really wanted to do was give in to whatever he asked of her.

In an effort to hold on to some semblance of normality, she said unsteadily, 'You could have told me I was adopted.'

'Oh, yeah.' Matt had to smile at that, his lean face creasing into the attractive lines she knew so well. 'How would that conversation have gone, I wonder? Look, sweetheart, Sara's really my biological mother, right? But don't be alarmed because you're adopted, okay?'

Rachel felt a reluctant giggle stir in her throat. 'All the same...'

'All the same—what?' He gazed up at her, his hands slipping inside the hem of her shorts to cup the rounded curve of her bottom. 'Help me out. I'm dying here.'

Rachel quivered. 'Well, you knew I was adopted, and obviously thought I knew it, too. So why didn't you just tell me Sara was your mother?'

'Oh, that...'

'Yes, that.'

He pulled a wry face. 'I didn't deliberately set out to deceive you. But you were obviously looking for your mother, and I knew that as soon as you found her you'd probably leave.' He leant towards her and licked the delicate skin of her midriff. 'And I didn't want that to happen.'

Rachel's fingers lifted to curve around his face. 'Do you mean that?'

Matt uttered a hoarse sound. 'Dammit, of course I mean it,' he said roughly. 'Do you think I like the idea of you thinking I was involved with someone else?'

Rachel shook her head. 'I was so jealous!'

'Jealous?'

'Don't pretend you didn't know.'

'All I know is I've never felt this way before,' muttered Matt a little harshly. With an impatient exclamation, he came to his feet and pulled her fully into his arms.

His mouth found hers almost of its own volition. With one hand behind her head, and the other pressing her close against his aroused body, he took possession of her lips with a heated urgency that betrayed his hungry need. Wedging one leg between hers, he let her feel his erection, drew one of her hands to him so she could shape its pulsing length.

'God, I've needed this,' he muttered at last, his breathing laboured as he sought the sensitive hollow of her throat. 'Just tell me that you feel the same way, or I think I really will go crazy. This has been the longest three weeks of my whole life.'

'And mine,' whispered Rachel, winding her arms about his neck and lifting one leg to stroke her toes down his calf. 'I thought—well, you know what I thought. And finding out Sara was your mother...' She paused. 'Well, I was sure she would convince you to stay away from me.'

'Baby, a herd of wild horses couldn't have kept me away,' he told her fervently. 'As soon as I realised what Sara had told you, I couldn't wait to get on a flight to England.'

Then he was kissing her again, long drugging kisses that weakened her knees and inflamed her blood. The feel of his hard body, the clean male scent of his skin, the possessive touch of his hands, were all sending electric shocks throughout her body. Even the scratch of his night's stubble caused a delicious thrill of awareness to feather her spine.

At last Matt released her mouth again, to say raggedly, 'I want you.' His hands were beneath her tee shirt, and his thumbs were brushing the undersides of her breasts. Then he spread his palms over her nipples and added unsteadily, 'I want you naked, in a bed, with me...'

CHAPTER SIXTEEN

RACHEL's bed was still tumbled, the way she'd left it. The rosebuds on the pillowcases and duvet cover were typically her, and Matt gazed at the bed with a feeling of utter contentment. They were together, and that was the most satisfying thing of all.

It was easy to undress Rachel. Her tee shirt was soon tugged over her head, and the men's boxers were too big for her anyway. Releasing one button had them pooling about her ankles, and Matt took a few seconds just to look at her. This was the woman he'd been searching all his life for, he thought incredulously. And he could hardly believe she was his.

Or she would be, if he had anything to say about it.

His own clothes were less easily discarded. But with Rachel's help he was soon as naked as she was. Then, just for the hell of it, he lifted her into his arms and let her wrap those long legs about his hips.

It meant his erection was close against her bottom, and that was painful. But he could wait, he told himself. They had the rest of their lives together.

'D'you know how much I've wanted to be with you?' he demanded, resting his forehead against hers. He could feel her breasts crushed against his chest, her sweet scent surrounding him. 'I don't think I've had a moment's relaxation since you left.'

Rachel smiled. 'I thought you wanted to go to bed,' she murmured provocatively, and Matt growled deep in his throat.

'I do,' he told her huskily. 'I'm just prolonging the moment. And anticipating what I'm going to do to you.'

'And that would be...?'

'You'll find out,' he assured her, his tone thickening, and, stepping forward, he tumbled her into the bed.

Rachel giggled then, and scrambled away from him. But he crawled onto the bed after her, catching her ankle and turning her onto her back.

'Come here,' he ordered, imprisoning her wrists above her head with one hand. Then he allowed his free hand to stroke a sensuous path from her throat to her breasts and beyond.

She bucked when his fingers slid into her cleft. But she remembered the pleasure he'd given her and spread her legs in innocent provocation.

'Rachel,' he groaned, his arousal not proof against such sensual seduction, and he moved to lie between her legs. Now she could feel his erection pulsing against her stomach, and knew that any control he had was rapidly being eroded.

His mouth covered hers with an urgency that confirmed her suspicions, his tongue thrusting eagerly between her lips. Hot and demanding, it twined with hers, its plunging possession imitating, in so many ways, that other possession he intended to take of her body.

'You're mine,' he muttered, against her mouth. 'And I'm never going to let you go.'

'Promises, prom—' she began, but her teasing words were stifled by his kiss.

Not that she cared. Freeing her hands, she clutched his neck, her fingers tangling in the damp hair at his nape. It was the purest kind of delight to be this close to him again, to know that, whatever happened now, they were together.

He straddled her then, and she levered herself up on her elbows to look down at him. With a confidence she'd hardly known she possessed, she took him into her hand and allowed her fingers to slide along the velvety length of his shaft.

There was a pearl of moisture on its tip, and she knew instinctively what would please him. She used her thumb to remove it and then deliberately put her thumb in her mouth.

That was when Matt lost it. Bearing her back against the pillows, he buried himself in her slick sheath, his laboured breathing an indication of how hard it had been for him to hold back for so long.

'I love you,' he said in a shaken voice, and Rachel's nails dug possessively into his neck.

'I love you, too,' she whispered brokenly, and heard his groan of satisfaction as he buried his face between her breasts.

When he started to move again, Rachel needed no encouragement to move with him. And, although their lovemaking was curtailed when Matt's body convulsed with his release a moment later, Rachel was only seconds behind him.

'I'm sorry,' Matt groaned when he could speak again. 'I've wanted you for such a long time.'

'Me, too,' said Rachel unsteadily, winding her arms around his neck. 'But we have all the time in the world...'

They made love again, and then took a shower together and made love in the shower. Matt's soapy hands made a mockery of any attempt Rachel might have made to resist him, and by the time they tumbled back into bed again they were both exhausted.

They must have slept for a couple of hours, because when Rachel opened her eyes Matt was climbing into bed again, a tray containing two mugs of coffee and a thick ham and cheese bread roll in his hands.

'Hey,' he said, leaning down to kiss her. 'You hungry?'

Rachel dimpled. 'Are you?'

'I'm always hungry—for you,' he appended wryly. 'But we have to satisfy the inner beast as well as the outer one.'

Rachel smiled. 'Are you a beast?'

'You'd better believe it,' he said, setting the tray on his knees. 'I'm your beast, so you'd better get used to it.'

'I can't think of anything I'd like more,' she murmured, wriggling into a sitting position.

She saw Matt looking at her breasts, but this time she made no attempt to cover herself as she reached for one of the mugs. 'Mmm, you're going to love this. Instant coffee!'

'Sweetheart, I'd drink salt water if it would mean I could be here with you,' he said huskily. He paused. 'Did you mean what you said?'

Rachel arched one brow. 'What did I say?' she asked, but she knew exactly what he meant. 'Did you?'

'When I said I loved you?' Matt didn't prevaricate. 'Yeah, I meant it.'

'So did I,' she whispered, her breathing quickening automatically. But when he would have moved the tray aside, she added, 'May I share your sandwich?'

'Is that all you want to share?'

'For now,' she said teasingly. 'Do you realise it's nearly two o'clock?'

'So what? As you say, we've got all the time in the world.' He broke the roll in half and handed it to her. 'I make a pretty good sandwich, though I say it myself.'

'I can vouch for that,' agreed Rachel, after tasting it. 'Among other things.'

'What other things?'

'Matt!' She gave him a reproving look. 'Not now. We have to talk.' She bit her lip. 'I have the feeling my—*your* mother isn't going to be too happy about this.'

'Tough.' Matt was unsympathetic. 'She'll get used to it. What about your father? What will he think?'

Rachel took another bite of the roll. She chewed for a moment and then she said, 'I don't think he'll mind at all. He's only ever wanted my happiness.'

'I think I'm going to like him.'

'I hope you do.' Rachel took a sip of her coffee. 'I just hope he and Mum can resolve their differences.'

'Well, that's their affair.' Matt pulled a face as he tried his coffee, but he didn't put it down. 'I guess it was hard for your father when Sara insisted on keeping in touch with me.'

'Yes.' Rachel nodded. 'Particularly as he suspected your father still cared about her.'

'Oh, God!' Matt laughed now. 'Well, I can certainly reassure him on that score. No one regretted the incident with Sara more than Jacob. Oh, don't get me wrong. He never hesitated when it came to taking responsibility for what had happened. And when I was born he'd have moved heaven and earth to gain custody of his son—me. The fact that Sara didn't want to keep the baby made everything so much simpler.'

'So how did you feel when Sara started visiting you?'

'Honestly?' Matt grimaced. 'Weird.' He paused. 'I met her in New York the first time. She'd found out I was going to Princeton, and I guess she regarded that as neutral ground.' He shook his head. 'But, man, although I knew Diana wasn't my mother, she'd always been there. Sara was a stranger to me. And when she started criticising my father I didn't like that much either.'

'You must have got quite shock when she turned up on St Antoine.'

'You'd better believe it.' Matt put his coffee on the bedside table and relaxed back on his elbows. 'I'd honestly never thought she'd come there. She knew how Jacob felt about her. It was really bad taste, particularly as he'd been ill and wasn't really equipped to deal with her.'

'She stayed with you, didn't she?'

'Yeah.' Matt gave Rachel a rueful grin. 'I mean, I didn't want her there, but she couldn't stay at Jaracoba, and I didn't particularly want her talking about our relationship at the hotel.'

'So tell me about your house,' said Rachel, deciding they'd

said enough about Sara for the time being. 'Is it on the ocean, as—as my mother said?'

'Mmm.' Matt nodded. 'But you'll see it soon enough.'

'Will I?'

'I hope so.' He was solemn now. 'I want you to come back with me.'

'To St Antoine?'

'Well, it's going to be your home,' said Matt reasonably. 'I have no intention of leaving you here for Sara to corrupt you again.'

Rachel finished her coffee and put it back on the tray. 'She didn't actually corrupt me,' she ventured, but Matt was having none of it.

'She let you think you'd been having a relationship with your own brother,' he retorted grimly, turning to imprison her beneath him. 'I think that qualifies.'

Rachel lifted a hand to stroke back the tousled hair from his forehead. 'I'm so glad you're not my brother.'

Matt groaned. 'Don't even think about it.'

'But I don't know if I can come back with you,' she said reluctantly. 'I have a job. Responsibilities.'

'I'll find you a job on St Antoine.' Matt grinned. 'You can help my father write his memoir.'

'Oh, Matt...'

'Do you want to come?'

'Need you ask?'

'Okay. Just leave it to me, then. After what I've been through these last few weeks, handling your boss will be child's play.'

Rachel sighed. 'You make it sound so easy.'

'It *is* easy.' Matt pushed himself up onto his knees. 'Now, there's only one other thing I need to ask you...'

EPILOGUE

THEY were married at the small church in St Antoine three months later.

Matt would have had the ceremony the week after they returned to the island. But Diana, who was organising the event, said she needed more time to ensure that Rachel had a day to remember.

'And me?' Matt had said, and Diana had given him a playful smile.

'I think all your days are going to be days to remember from now on,' she said lightly. 'Now, go and tell your father his lunch is ready.'

Rachel loved Matt's house as soon as she saw it. Unlike Jaracoba, it was a sprawling beach bungalow, with over a dozen reception rooms and half a dozen bedrooms besides. There was a fully equipped gym, and a pool, and it was only yards from Mango Cove, where Matt had taken her on her first morning on the island.

'I wanted to show you my house then,' he confessed. 'But, apart from the fact that Sara was there, you didn't exactly encourage me to pursue a relationship.'

'And did you want to?'

'Oh, yeah.' Matt was very definite about that. 'I knew I wanted you the moment I saw you. But I've already told you that. Stop fishing.'

'And I didn't know it, but I wanted you, too,' admitted Rachel shyly. 'What a fool I was.'

'Well, you're my fool now,' teased Matt, earning a playful slap. 'And I love you, little fool. For ever and a day.'

The wedding was a huge success. Rachel wore a cream moiré gown, with an overskirt and train of pearl-studded silk. She carried a bouquet of roses and baby's breath, with Matt's engagement ring—an exquisite diamond solitaire—her only jewellery.

Matt, in a black tuxedo, looked big and dark and handsome, and when he placed his wedding ring on her finger Rachel was the envy of every woman present.

Rachel's parents attended the wedding. They stayed at the hotel, and, although they were not exactly reconciled, they were not exactly estranged either. Aunt Laura was there, to give the happy couple her endorsement, and all in all Rachel thought the day was everything she could have wished for.

She and Matt spent an idyllic honeymoon in Italy, and then returned home in time for the hurricane season.

'I told you not all days were lovely on St Antoine,' Matt said one morning, waking to find his wife seated on the windowseat of their bedroom, watching torrential rain falling past the windows.

'Uh, no, that was Amalie,' retorted Rachel, smiling as her husband got out of bed and came to join her. 'But, anyway, I don't mind the rain. So long as it doesn't last too long.'

'It won't.' Matt seated himself behind her and drew her back into his embrace. He was naked, and she felt his morning erection nudging her bottom. 'How are you feeling?'

'Better since I threw up,' she admitted ruefully. 'Did I wake you?'

'No,' he lied, but she knew he was aware of every aspect of her pregnancy.

He'd already expressed the opinion that they should have waited, that he didn't want to share her with anyone else.

But Rachel knew what he was really worried about was the fact that her biological mother had died just after giving her birth.

'I'll be fine, you know,' she murmured, tipping her head back against his shoulder. Her hands curved over the slight swell of her stomach. 'Besides, I want your baby. I want to feel it growing inside me. To know that he or she is the ultimate proof of how much I love you.'

'I know.'

Matt bent to caress her shoulder with his lips. He wasn't convinced, and she knew it, but she also knew he'd do anything to make her happy—and if that meant lying about his own fears so be it.

In fact, their child was born just six months later, in the bedroom they used when they stayed at Jaracoba. Matt had wanted Rachel to have the baby in the hospital in town, but the doctor had agreed that in the circumstances there was no reason why she shouldn't have the baby where she chose. And having Jacob and Diana around was definitely a bonus.

In consequence, Matt was the first to hold their son when he came, kicking and screaming, into the world.

'A lusty infant,' declared the doctor admiringly, and Rachel, who had insisted on having the baby by natural means, gave him a tired but triumphant smile.

'Like his father,' she said softly, earning a look that promised retribution later from her husband.

'He's beautiful,' she said, when Matt came to lay their child in her arms. 'Isn't he?'

'Like his mother,' agreed Matt, perching on the bed beside her. He bent to kiss her flushed face. 'Did I tell you I love you?'

'Not for the past couple of hours,' she murmured, feeling his arm slipping around her. 'Hmm, shall we call him Jacob, after your father?'

'Jake,' said Matt, shortening it. 'Yeah. Jake Brody. I like it.'

Jacob Brody was thrilled to hear they were going to call the baby after him. He and Diana would make perfect grandparents, and even Sara and Ralph appeared at the baby's christening.

'Do you think we brought those two together again?' asked Matt, as he and Rachel strolled on the beach at Mango Cove after the celebrations were over.

'Well, they brought us together,' murmured Rachel softly. 'And that's the most important thing, don't you think?'

And Matt agreed.

are proud to present our...

Book of the Month

St Piran's: Penhally's Wedding of the Year & St Piran's: Rescued Pregnant Cinderella

from Mills & Boon®
Medical™ Romance 2-in-1

ST PIRAN'S: THE WEDDING OF THE YEAR
by Caroline Anderson
GP Nick Tremayne and midwife Kate Althorp have an unfulfilled love that's lasted a lifetime. Now, with their little boy fighting for his life in St Piran's Hospital…can they find their way back to one another?

ST PIRAN'S: RESCUING PREGNANT CINDERELLA
by Carol Marinelli
Dr Izzy Bailey is single and pregnant when she meets the gorgeous neo-natal nurse Diego Ramirez. When she goes into labour dangerously early Diego is there to rescue her… Could this be the start of her fairytale?

Available 3rd December

*Something to say about our Book of the Month?
Tell us what you think!*

millsandboon.co.uk/community
facebook.com/romancehq
twitter.com/millsandboonuk

Discover Pure Reading Pleasure with

Visit the Mills & Boon website for all the latest in romance

Buy all the latest releases, backlist and eBooks

Find out more about our authors and their books

Join our community and chat to authors and other readers

Free online reads from your favourite authors

Win with our fantastic online competitions

Sign up for our free monthly eNewsletter

Tell us what you think by signing up to our reader panel

Rate and review books with our star system

www.millsandboon.co.uk

Follow us at twitter.com/millsandboonuk

Become a fan at facebook.com/romancehq

2 FREE BOOKS
AND A SURPRISE GIFT

We would like to take this opportunity to thank you for reading this Mills & Boon® book by offering you the chance to take TWO more specially selected books from the Modern™ series absolutely FREE! We're also making this offer to introduce you to the benefits of the Mills & Boon® Book Club™—

- **FREE home delivery**
- **FREE gifts and competitions**
- **FREE monthly Newsletter**
- **Exclusive Mills & Boon Book Club offers**
- **Books available before they're in the shops**

Accepting these FREE books and gift places you under no obligation to buy, you may cancel at any time, even after receiving your free books. Simply complete your details below and return the entire page to the address below. You don't even need a stamp!

YES Please send me 2 free Modern books and a surprise gift. I understand that unless you hear from me, I will receive 4 superb new books every month for just £3.30 each, postage and packing free. I am under no obligation to purchase any books and may cancel my subscription at any time. The free books and gift will be mine to keep in any case.

Ms/Mrs/Miss/Mr _____ Initials _____

Surname _____

Address _____

_____

_____ Postcode _____

E-mail _____

Send this whole page to: Mills & Boon Book Club, Free Book Offer, FREEPOST NAT 10298, Richmond, TW9 1BR

Offer valid in UK only and is not available to current Mills & Boon Book Club subscribers to this series. Overseas and Eire please write for details.. We reserve the right to refuse an application and applicants must be aged 18 years or over. Only one application per household. Terms and prices subject to change without notice. Offer expires 28th February 2011. As a result of this application, you may receive offers from Harlequin Mills & Boon and other carefully selected companies. If you would prefer not to share in this opportunity please write to The Data Manager, PO Box 676, Richmond, TW9 1WU.

Mills & Boon® is a registered trademark owned by Harlequin Mills & Boon Limited. Modern™ is being used as a trademark. The Mills & Boon® Book Club™ is being used as a trademark.